DARK FOLK
edited by
PAUL KARCZAG

D1127629

TABLE OF CONTENTS

DARK FOLK

Editor: Paul Karczag

Supervising Editor: Bill Fawcett

Copy Editor: Darrelyn Karczag

Coordinating Editor: P. Bromley

Internal Art and Maps: Gerald O'Malley, Jim Clouse, and David B. Bromley

Cover Illustration: Blind Corner © 1982 Janny Wurts
Janny Wurts is the author of Sorcerer's Legacy, available from Ace SF

TROLLS . . . . .Paul Karczag and Steve Morrison

ORC CULTURE . . . . .Robert Lynn Asprin

ORCS . . . . .Les Kay

GNOLLS . . . . .Arthur Miller and Irwin Goldstein
Adventure . . . .Irwin Goldstein

KOBOLDS . . . . .Alan Nudelman

GOBLINS . . . . .Susan Khas

©Mayfair Games Inc. 1983
All Rights Reserved

---

 and RoleAids are trademarks for roleplaying aids and
adventures published by Mayfair Games Inc.

Mayfair Games Inc. • P.O. Box 48539 • Niles, IL • 60648

Introduction

Welcome to the world of the Dark Folk. If you have ever wondered how Kobolds, Goblins, Orcs, or Trolls live and are motivated, this is the book for you. Hopefully, reading this book will allow you to instill more depth into any campaign that you participate in; as a game-master, you will be able to employ the strategies and tactics used by the various races, while as a player, you can be prepared to counter the schemes perpetrated by them. The various races depicted within are not particularly friendly or fun-loving, but they are interesting!

Each section of this book delivers specifics about a race in two ways. First, there is a presentation of the cultural heritage of each race and a description of their everyday lives and attitudes. Second, an adventure among members of that race is presented. Playing these adventures will offer many additional insights into the abilities of each different race.

THE CONTINENT OF MAMARYL

Since the adventures must take place somewhere, we now present you with the island continent of Mamaryl. A map of the continent is provided showing all pertinent geographic features and the location of the major cities and trade routes. Beyond the short description of each city that follows, very little information is provided so that any game-master may design the continent to suit his or her own campaign. If you wish, any adventure may be easily installed into your own campaign, merely by changing the location names. Additional information about each city can be found in the adventure backgrounds.

Here are the starting locations for each adventure:

RACE	TOWN
Troll	Jovian Falls
Orc	Jovian Falls
Gnolls	Jovian Delta
Kobolds	Aspregull
Goblins	Illaria

Jovian Falls

Jovian Falls was established as a center of trade by the imperial government about 200 years ago. Caravans from the southern and western cities deliver a wide variety of goods that are loaded aboard ships and taken to Jovian Delta, for eventual shipment to the imperial capital on Spider Isle.

Further specific information on the history and background of Jovian Falls can be found in the introduction to the Troll Adventure.

Since Jovian Falls is referenced in more than one adventure in this book, we are presenting a few specific facts about the town. Also provided are charts so that the exact nature of any building can be determined.

Both bridges spanning the Jovian River are 25' wide and are made of heavily reinforced wood and stone. At the island end of the bridges, two River Trolls collect the bridge tolls: 2 cp per individual, 3 cp per animal, 3 cp per cart, and 1 gp per wagon load of goods to be sold.

The palace is normally closed to casual visitors. Important merchants and nobles known to the Duke have passes which allow them access to him on demand. All other individuals seeking an audience with the Duke must file a petition in one of the government buildings.

All guard barracks are 2 levels high, house 12d10 men, and have ballistas or catapults mounted on their roofs.

An extensive sewer system runs under the city; it may be entered or exited through any wrecked building. All sewers are made of cut stone and are 5' in diameter. The palace sewer system is protected by metal grates with 6" openings.

The dock area, outside the town, is neither guarded nor patrolled. It is considered to be a free port and people living outside the town often purchase goods here as no city taxes need be paid. As might be expected, thieves and dishonest merchants abound in this area.

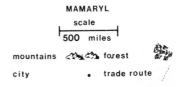

BUILDING GENERATION TABLES

In Jovian Falls, 35% of the buildings are obviously business establishments, 50% are obvious residences, and 15% do not have a readily apparent function. This last type of building could be a business, residence, temple, government office, or a combination of several offices. Small buildings have a maximum wall length of 30'; medium buildings have a maximum wall length of 60'; and, naturally, large buildings exceed 60' in wall length. All buildings have ceilings that range from 7-12' in height.

BUILDING TYPE

01 - 56	SMALL BUILDING	
	01-75	Residential
	76-89	Commercial
	90-00	Other
57 - 89	MEDIUM BUILDING	
	01-15	Residential
	16-76	Commercial
	77-00	Other
90 - 00	LARGE BUILDING	
	01-27	Residential
	28-91	Commercial
	92-00	Other

BUILDING FRAME

01-50	Wood
51-79	Cut Stone
80-89	Brick
90-00	Mix of above

SMALL BUILDINGS

Structure

01-30	1 level high
31-65	1 level plus basement
66-80	1 level plus basement and garden - 30% have wells
81-95	2 levels high, no basement
96-00	2 levels high plus basement - 25% have gardens

Occupants

	Residential	*Commercial*	*Other*
1	Gate Keeper	Gambling House	Animal Trainer
2	Butcher	Locksmith	Stable
3	Weaver	Bar	Sage
4	Tarot Reader	Boot Store	Poet
5	Merchant	Tailor	Hangman
6	Merchant	Carver	Scribe
7	Thief	Baker	Bard
8	Boarding House	Potter	Music
9	Courtesan	Glass Blower	Shrine
10	Customs Agent	Fletcher's Shop	Juggler

MEDIUM BUILDINGS

Structure

01-30	1 level high
31-60	2 levels high
61-70	2 levels plus basement - 25% have wells
71-75	2 levels plus basement - 25% have wells; 30% have secret or hidden rooms
76-85	2 levels and a cave entrance from the sewers
86-90	2 levels with stable - 60% have basements
96-00	3 levels with stable and basement

Occupants

	Residential	*Commercial*	*Other*
1	Town Clerk	Ale Shop	Empty/For Rent
2	Courtesan	Bar	Bath House
3	Author	Seamstress	Funeral House
4	Councils	Stables	Barracks
5	Councilor	Silver/Goldsmith	Barracks
6	Fighter	Wheelwright	House of Families
7	Musician	Baker	Theater
8	Cleric	Boat Maker	Artist
9	Poor Noble	Gen'l Merchant	Guild House
10	Tavern Owner	Tavern w/rooms for rent	Gov't Building

LARGE BUILDINGS

Structure

01-30	1 level high
31-40	1 level high with basement and balcony
41-55	2 levels high with a well and wine cellar - 20% have stables
56-70	2 levels high
71-82	2 levels high tower on a 1 level building plus balcony
83-95	3 level building with well and stable
96-00	Split level 1-2 level building with a garden roof and well

Occupants

	Residential	*Commercial*	*Other*
1	Merchant	Winery	Pleasure Palace
2	Sage	Carpenter	Stables
3	Military Officer	Jeweler	Merchant
4	Merchant	Armorer	Merchant
5	Judge	Guild House	Religious
6	Noble	Sail Maker	High Level MU
7	Noble	Warehouse	Thief
8	Merchant	Warehouse	Jail
9	Ship Captain	General Store	Temple
10	Dishonest Customs Agent	Auctioneer	Fortune Teller

ASPREGULL

The city of Aspregull is named in honor of its founding father, the arch-mage Aspregull the Strict. Remains in the older portions of town are suspected of being over 800 years old; city records were kept after Aspregull departed from his manor, about 650 years ago. He has never returned.

Early settlers built their homes and farms near Aspregull's manor. There was never any question as to who was the protector and sovereign lord of the land. Word rapidly spread of the rich, peaceful area and many diverse peoples and races helped to found a new city. It is suspected that the pressures established by a burgeoning population forced Aspregull to suddenly depart.

Today, the town of Aspregull produces food and many hand-crafted items for the rest of the continent. A council of representatives, chosen from the guilds, rules the town with an iron fist. There are no loose gold pieces found among the guildsmen.

There are over 8,000 individuals in Aspregull and 1,200

farmers in the surrounding valleys. There is a saying, "You can get anything you need or want in Aspregull. Just name the right price!" Most shops are open late at night and have notices posted stating where the owner can be reached after hours.

JOVIAN DELTA

Jovian Delta is the largest seaport in Mamaryl. It serves as a commercial focal point for trade arriving overland, from the outer islands, and from the city of Jovian Falls. Any merchandise to be shipped to the imperial capital, on Spider Isle must first pass through the imperial customs offices located on the waterfront. Those goods are then shipped aboard heavily guarded imperial cargo ships. For further information about Jovian Delta, see the introduction to the Gnoll Adventure.

BRIGANDSPORT

Brigandsport, originally founded as a pirate base, possesses a fine harbor guarded by treacherous reefs. For many years, the safe passage through the reefs remained a secret to all but the pirate captains. The brigands raided ships and terrorized settlements until a force led by Murphy the Mad marched overland to lay seige to the city, while an imperial fleet commanded by Lord Ivram Hertzog kept the pirate fleet bottled up behind their reefs. After a six-month seige, the pirates capitulated.

Once the pirate menace had been eliminated, barbarian fishermen were allowed to settle in Brigandsport. Safe passages were blasted through the reefs by mages from the imperial staff and a fishing port was established. Today, Brigandsport is the second largest port in Mamaryl with a population of approximately 8,000 free citizens and 2,500 slaves. The city is ruled by an imperial governor and guarded by imperial troops; as the largest city in the vicinity of Spider Isle, recent emperors have enforced a policy of "maintaining Brigandsport as a friendly city."

PEREVU

The city of Perevu is a theocracy governed by a council of priests representing all religions. The speaker for the council is the high priest whose religion has the most followers at the end of the calendar year. Thus, Perevu, in addition to being a primary source of clerics in Mamaryl, is a hotbed of religious fervor. As might be expected, the city is divided into many factions and all settlers and visitors must stay in the proper section of town or face a stiff penalty for fraudulently representing themselves. The

current speaker has held the post for more than twenty years; he represents the followers of Bacchus, the god of wine and merriment.

At any time, there will be 300-600 student priests learning spells, texts, and rituals in the city. The permanent population consists of 3,500 shopkeepers, craftsmen, guildsmen and farmers, and 250-300 resident priests. Due to the aggressive religous nature of the populace, barbarian tribes in the area give Perevu a wide berth. The city has not been attacked in several centuries. Also, slavery has been outlawed in Perevu; anyone bringing slaves into the territory governed by the council will be immediately sentenced to 1-10 years at hard labor per slave owned (slaves are immediately granted freedom).

KINTOCK

The city of Kintock is a rather unremarkable agricultural center. Produce from many miles around is brought to Kintock for shipment throughout the realm. The area was originally settled by Amir Kintock; Amir XVII, Count of Kintock is a bearded jovial man in his mid-seventies. He inherited the title to the city and several thousand square miles surrounding it when his father died twenty years ago. Count Kintock has established a feudal relationship with the farmers and shopkeepers on his land; he maintains a large standing army to insure peace in the area in return for a tithe of their production.

The land around Kintock is quite rich. Though the city is situated on the Rough River, no trade passes up the river because it contains many waterfalls and much white water. There are approximately 4,500 residents in Kintock, and another 6,000 farmers in the fertile valleys to the north.

MARKOS LANDING

Markos Landing, founded as the result of a shipwreck, is now the third largest seaport on the continent. The original settlers, sailors and slaves, built a thriving community in an area where game was plentiful and natural stands of wild fruit grew in profusion. When the wreck of their ship was finally spotted by a merchantman seeking shelter from a storm, none of the settlers wished to leave.

In fact, they hired several mages to expand their natural harbor and to build a firm seawall.

The best shipwrights and drydocks in Mamaryl are in this city. The emperor has a standing order for one warship to be built every two years. Many merchants also have placed orders for the sturdy, finely-crafted ships produced in the Markos Landing Shipyards. Markos Landing also exports most of the citrus crop produced in Mamaryl.

The city is governed by an elected Captain who rules the city with an iron hand. All the leading citizens sit on a council of advisors; other city officials hold the title of First Officer, Second Officer, Third Officer, etc. There are approximately 4,500 free citizens and 8,000 slaves in Markos Landing.

ILLARIA

Illaria, the elven capital, was established as a center of learning. Many different subjects are studied and taught in this city, located deep in the heart of the Illarian Forest.

KINDAIRY

Kindairy is best known for the quantity and quality of liquor produced by the local populace. Almost everyone in the area is constantly involved in the production, dispensing, or consumption of alcohol in all its various forms. Wine, beer, and ale are all produced in prodigious quantities. The most potent brew produced is called Kindairy Dew. Distilled from grain and a few secret ingredients, Kindairy Dew packs quite a wallop and is in great demand throughout Mamaryl. Local breweries are often looking for guards to protect caravans taking Kindairy Dew to other parts of the continent. As might be expected, the clerics of Kindairy have standing orders to ship most of their product to the city of Perevu.

The population of Kindairy is 8,500, of which only half is sober at any one time. The city has an elected representative government, with the chief official having the title of Brewmaster. The Brewmaster is expected to attend all public functions and to serve as the official tester as each new batch is released for sale. He will assign each batch a rating, with the highly-rated batches bringing exorbitant amounts on the open market.

TROLLS

By Paul Karczag and Steve Morrison

Found throughout myth and fantasy, trolls are creatures designed to strike fear into the hearts of children and young adults. Like the Bogey Man, these elusive creatures wait in the shadows to grab bad children, drag them off to their foul lairs and to devour them. (We find it curious that while trolls are touted to be creatures of great evil, they are reputed to take only bad children, hence their actions place them on the side of law and goodness, not against it.)

Much of this same stigma has been carried over into the world of fantasy gaming. Trolls are characterized as large stupid, ugly creatures who are "known" to be terribly evil enemies of all mankind. As a result, trolls have become instant targets marked for extermination by overeager bands of adventurers. No interaction (other than with the edge of a sword) is deemed necessary, for the troll is too stupid to do anything other than wantonly attack other humanoids. Like most "facts" put forth by non-comprehending adversaries, the true nature of trolls needs to be examined under the unbiased lens of knowledge and illuminated by the light of the lamp of truth. Perhaps then the world will understand the troll, a species much like man, adapted to all climes of existence and with many different attitudes (or alignments, if you wish) toward other living creatures.

HISTORY: THE ELDER TROLL RACE

The elder race of trolls, a small (4½ to 5 foot tall) race of humanoids varying in color from green to brown, were originally forest dwellers. Competent miners, they were able to excavate shelters for themselves and thus had an early advantage over some of the other dark races, for they could live where they chose, not having to rely on natural caverns as did the other races. For this reason, it has been hypothesized that trolls are an offshoot of the Mountain Dwarves (possibly a magic-user's experiment gone awry, or the result of potion misciability). There is no conclusive evidence of this or any other theory, and the origin of the trolls remains a mystery.

The trolls of old lived in large societal groups with several tribes ruled by a council of Chiefs and Shamans. Seldom travelling far from home, their only contact with the other dark races came about as a result of trade. Living in the forests, the trolls, while not overly intelligent, did exhibit curiousity about their surroundings and quickly learned about the useful properties of the many plants, herbs, barks, roots, lichen, and moss which grew in wild profusion. They learned to utilize these various substances in producing healing potions and salves for which they found a ready market among their forest neighbors. As a result of their newly found talent, the trolls began to travel more extensively, marketing their herbs, powders, and roots to all who could purchase them. Slowly, the great tribes broke up, dispersing to all corners of the known world. Adapting readily to vastly different living conditions, various sub-species developed. Knowledge not used was

lost, and the old ways were rediscovered. Settling in new regions and establishing large tribes took many centuries, for trolls moved in small groups, migrating to new locations only a few miles distant until a fairly large area was populated.

Since the ancient trolls were a warlike race, highly ritualistic and individual combat amongst tribal members was a daily occurance. The fights were to the death, and inevitably this worked to strengthen the race. The hardiest, strongest, fleetest, and smartest survived, insuring the survival of the troll in days when other races perished without a trace. Highly courageous (or foolhardy), trolls were feared by the other denizens of the forest. Though many other creatures were larger and stronger, the regenerative power of the troll made it impossible for the other creatures to defeat them, and the trolls quickly carved out a place of respect for themselves among all with whom they dealt.

As the outward migration continued, the old ways were not forgotten, merely adapted to the new geographic and climatic conditions. Their social and inter-racial relations changed, as necessary, for survival.

J. CLOUSE '82

INTRODUCTION

As noted before, trolls now exist in every climate habitable by man. They are found in the far frozen north, the hot arid deserts, the mountain heights, the river depths, and deep in tropical forests. Trolls have proven to be very adaptable and able to survive under the harshest of living conditions. In each of the following sections, the information presented first will generally be characteristic of all trolls. Any variance within the various sub-races will then be discussed.

We shall examine many types of trolls and shall attempt to point out their habitats, diet, social attitudes and, most importantly, their interactions with the creatures around them.

GENERAL INFORMATION ABOUT TROLLS

COMMON TROLLS, comprising 35% of the troll race, are the most frequently encountered type of troll. They stand 7-8' tall and have green to brown coloration. They are the only troll type to wander the countryside in small groups. For some reason, they have never organized themselves into large, sedentary tribes like the other troll sub-races. Roving predators, they utilize abandoned caves, haystacks, or large trees for shelter and survive by hunting small animals and stealing livestock from lonely farms.

Least civilized of all the trolls, they wear neither clothes nor armor, but have a natural AC: 5 due to their thick hide. Favored weapons include clubs and spears, though, if unarmed, they will attack with both claws and a vicious bite (1d4, 1d4, 1d8 points of damage). Their bite, if successful, has a 5% chance of causing disease. Though low in intelligence, they are quite cunning and prefer to ambush opponents from the rear. They regenerate at 3 HTK per round.

A typical band of Common Trolls will consist of the following:

	AC	HTK	NUMBER PRESENT
Chief	3	6d8	1 (80%) or 2 (20%)
Sub-leaders	4	5d8	2 (60%) or 1 (40%)
Shamans	7	4-7d8	1 (50%), 2 (30%), or none (20%)
Witchdoctor	5	4-6d8	3 (50%), 2 (30%), or 1 (20%)
Common Trolls	5	4d8	5d8

DESERT TROLLS, representing 4% of the troll race, are rarely seen. They live in the hot, dry deserts, deep below the burning sands in vast labyrinths just above the water level. They regenerate 4 HTK per round; stand 5-6' tall and range in color from tan to light orange. Blending easily into the sandy terrain, they attack intruders with spears, bolas, and large knives. Desert Trolls will never use unarmed attacks on an enemy; they are strictly reserved for ritual inter-tribal combat. They are highly intelligent, very dextrous (attack twice per round using weapons), and extremely patient.

Desert Troll society is comprised of three diverse groups. The Providers raise snakes, fungus, and succulents in the subterranean caverns. The Scouts, travelling alone, patrol wide areas of desert in search of game animals, travellers, and caravans. The Warriors protect the caverns from invasion and attack caravans crossing the deserts. These caravans provide the trolls with food, trade goods, and slaves.

FOREST TROLLS are often mistaken for Common Trolls as their coloration is similar and they also shun clothing. Comprising 15% of the troll population, Forest Trolls stand 8-9' tall, are of average intelligence and have 3d8+6 HTK. Like most trolls, they regenerate 3 HTK per round and are excellent hunters. Forest Trolls can be found

J. CLOUSE '82

living in all parts of the forest including caverns, nests high in trees, large huts near the rivers, and hollows hidden under large piles of rocks. Masters of camouflage, their lairs can be difficult to locate even for the most experienced rangers.

They often wear leather armor over their tough hide, but seldom use shields; thus they are AC: 4. These trolls use clubs, spears, and short swords as weapons and train constantly to sharpen their skills. When unarmed, they have three attacks (claw, claw, bite) for 2-5, 2-5, 2-8 points of damage.

RIVER TROLLS, unknown until about 200 years ago, have adapted themselves to life underwater by developing gills located in their armpits. They have not lost their ability to breath air, but after extended periods (6-8 hours) on dry land, their skin dries out and they must apply fish oil (or its equivalent) to alleviate the discomfort. River Trolls regenerate at 3 HTK per round as long as their skins are moist; once they dry out, they can only regenerate at a rate of 1 HTK per round. Hardier than most other trolls, they have 5d8+2 HTK and range in color from green to aqua. They stand 9' tall and represent 5% of the troll population. Accustomed to underwater life, River Trolls favor tridents, spears, and short swords, attacking three times every two rounds. Due to their environment, they do not wear armor or carry shields, but their high dexterity gives them a natural AC: 6. Unless they are given no option, they will not engage in unarmed combat.

8

HILL TROLLS, ranging in color from brown to grey and tan; stand merely 6' tall, and have 6d8 HTK. As the smallest and weakest members of the troll sub-race, they have been driven from their forest homes to find refuge in the hills. They do not use armor or shields, but have a natural AC: 5. When using their favored weapons, clubs or spears, they have one attack per round. Unarmed, they attack like other trolls (claw, claw, bite) and do 2-5, 2-5, 2-8 points of damage.

Unlike their brethren, they favor frontal attack at a full charge. This lack of strategy, along with their warlike nature and hatred of other races, has brought about their near extinction (they form only 2% of the troll population) and are consequently, are very rarely seen. Depending on well-concealed and guarded caves for survival, they are quite adept at constructing pits, snares, and deadfalls and hiding in shadows. They regenerate 3 HTK per round, but in recent years, a number (40% estimate) have been born with impaired or no regenerative powers; this is also thought to be a contributing factor in their demise.

MOUNTAIN TROLLS represent 15% of the troll population and are the largest and meanest of their kind, standing 9-10' tall. Their coloration, ranging from reddish brown to green-grey, allows them to easily blend into the background of their mountain environment. They have 8d8 HTK and regenerate at 3 HTK per round. They wear no armor and carry no shields, having a natural AC: 3. Their mountain lairs are difficult to find and easy to defend; Mountain Trolls seemingly have no fear of any man or beast. They favor spears, longswords, and halberds, but when disarmed, they rely on their three natural attacks (claw, claw, bite), doing 2-7, 2-7, 1-12 points of damage. Mountain Trolls dislike daylight, and usually hunt by night; there is only a 10% chance that they will be encountered before nightfall. They have evolved ultravision (in addition to their infravision), which gives them clear vision even on the darkest nights.

FROZEN WASTE TROLLS, represent 12% of the troll population and stand 7-8' tall. They are the hardiest of the race, though by no means the largest or strongest. Covered with a dull grey to white fur, they are ideally suited for camouflage in the snow-covered wastelands. They wear heavy furs in lieu of armor, are AC: 3 (in part due to their tough skins), and have 8d8 HTK.

Frozen Waste Trolls favor spears, halberds, and large double-bladed axes, do appropriate damage by weapon type. They fall back on their natural attacks, which deliver 1-6, 1-6, 1-12 points of damage, only when disarmed. Their regenerative ability appears to have been augmented by the climate, for they regenerate 4 HTK per round.

DARK TROLLS, least well-known of the troll sub-races, are by far the vilest of the race. Fortunately for humankind, they prefer life deep underground, rarely venturing forth. Representing 6% of the troll race, they are dark brown, dark grey, or black in color, stand 7-8' tall and have 5d8 HTK.

The only troll race capable of manufacturing weapons, they rely on these weapons very heavily, and seldom use their normal attack abilities. They are often seen wearing chain or studded leather armor, carrying a large shield and brandishing a broadsword, bastardsword, or a two-handed sword (comfortably weilded in one hand). They are masters at hiding in shadows and moving silently; they surprise opponents on a roll of 1-4 on a d6. They regenerate at 3 HTK per round and have virtually no fear of fire; thus making them a formidable opponent.

HALF BREEDS share the characteristics of their parent's troll subclass. Both Giant and Two Headed Trolls integrate well into their parent's tribe and are rarely seen outside troll society. Trorcs are often alienated from their parent's tribe and are usually found in groups separate from normal trolls and appear to breed true among themselves.

GIANT TROLLS, are the result of trolls mating with Giants. Due to sterility and an inherent inability to regenerate, they represent 1% of the population. Though they are quite cunning, their great size, ranging 10-12' in height, and strength are offset by their low intelligence. They wear animal skins in lieu of armor, have a natural

AC: 4, and fight with great double edged battleaxes, gigantic tree branches, and heavy lances. Like true Giants, they also will hurl rocks and boulders for 2d8 points of damage. Giant Trolls, not surprisingly, often become Chiefs or Sub-leaders in their tribe.

TWO HEADED TROLLS, representing 2% of the population, are the product of matings between Trolls and Ettins. However, unlike Giant Trolls, they are able to breed; there is a 25% that the offspring of a troll and a Two Headed Troll will result in an offspring with two heads.

Two Headed Trolls are independent and highly intelligent in each head, and often become Witchdoctor/-Shamans. This allows them to remain aloof from combat, for they stand 8'-9' tall and are relatively weak compared to most trolls. Standing behind the fighting forces, they cast their spells to strengthen their troops and weaken the opposition. They do not wear armor, have a natural AC: 4, and carry a club or heavy staff for defense. Two Headed Trolls have the alignment ranges of the sub-class into which they are born and are a range higher in intelligence.

J CLOUSE '82

TRORCS are an awful cross breed between an Orc and a Troll. From their Orc parentage, they have inherited a complete hatred of Elves and an attitude of extreme cruelty toward all weaker life forms. From their troll parentage, they have inherited improved infravision (90') and regeneration (only 1 hit per turn). They are large (8' tall), Chaotic Evil, and of average to low intelligence. Trorcs speak Orc, Troll, and the languages of chaos and evil. They live to be about 75 years of age.

Trorcs are red, green, yellow, or brown in color with dull, black eyes and are somewhat fire-resistant (+2 to save vs. fire, but -2 to save vs cold) and immune to Fear spells. They are dextrous (+2 with bows) and are competant guards as they are completely fearless. They will use their bows until close melee is enjoined; then the bows are discarded. In combat, they usually (85%) have only one attack, a vicious bite with needle-sharp teeth for 2-12 points damage. The rest of the time, they will try three attacks, two claws for 1-4 each and then the bite for 2-8; if both claws hit, the bite (if it succeeds, it will be at +3) will do 2-24 points damage.

For each 12 Trorcs, there will be a 5d8+5 Sub-leader. The leaders usually carry both a sword and a dagger and can use both each melee round. For each 20 Trorcs, there will be one 8d8 Chief, who usually carries two swords and uses both each melee round.

TRIBAL LEADERSHIPS

Troll leadership, calm and relatively unchanging to the casual observer, is a subtle balance between the three factions: the Chief and Sub-leaders, the Shamans, and the Witchdoctors.

A troll Witchdoctor inherits his occupation at birth. Both males and females receive the symbol of Witchdoctors, a stylistic red flame, tatooed on the back of the left hand, when they are a few days old. Training continues through the life of the troll, with the eldest practicing troll in a tribe receiving the title of Tribal Curate. Females receive equal training and can serve as a Tribal Curate.

Witchdoctors never have a choice of occupation; the threat of immediate execution hangs over the head of any troll Witchdoctor who does not use his talent willingly on demand. Witchdoctors, powerful as they are, are not usually granted any special status within the tribe; they do not ordinarily receive choice cuts of meat and are required to join the hunting and root-gathering parties like ordinary trolls. However, if a Witchdoctor feels that conditions are intolerable within his tribe, he is free by troll law to take up residence within another tribe and will suffer no repercussions. If an elder troll Witchdoctor leaves, the entire troll family (all Witchdoctors) usually goes along; therefore most Witchdoctors receive better treatment than is required by Troll Law.

The duties of a troll Witchdoctor include: preparing healing potions and salves under the directions of a Shaman, carving and enchanting charms, assisting in the fabrication of magic weapons, and aiding hunting and war parties with their magic. As their skill level increases, a Witchdoctor gains an additional 1d8 HTK per skill level.

The Tribal Curate can play a pivotal part in the selection of a troll Chieftain. See the section below for more details.

Troll Shamans, unlike the Witchdoctors, occupy a position of recognized power and authority. The Tribal Shaman, usually the most devout and powerful Troll

WITCHDOCTOR'S SPELLS

	Spell Level	
Skill	1	2
1	2	-
2	2	1
3	3	2
4	4	3

	Common	Desert	Forest	River	Hill	Mountain	Frozen Waste	Dark	Giant	Two Headed	Trorcs
Relative No.:	35%	4%	15%	5%	2%	15%	12%	6%	1%	2%	3%

AC/HTK

	Common	Desert	Forest	River	Hill	Mountain	Frozen Waste	Dark	Giant	Two Headed	Trorcs
Normal:	5/4d8	4/3d8	4/3d8+6	6/5d8+2	5/6d8	3/8d8+6	3/8d8	1/5d8	4/8d8	4/7d8	5/4d8+2
Sub-leader:	4/5d8	3/4d8	3/4d8+6	5/6d8+2	4/7d8	2/9d8+6	2/9d8	0/6d8	3/9d8	3/8d8	5/5d8+5
Chief:	3/6d8	2/5d8	2/5d8+6	4/7d8+2	3/8d8	1/10d8+6	1/10d8	-1/7d8	2/10d8	2/9d8	4/6d8

Highest Skill Level (add 1d8 per level)

	Common	Desert	Forest	River	Hill	Mountain	Frozen Waste	Dark	Giant	Two Headed	Trorcs
Shaman:	3	7	5	7	5	5	4	7	3	7	3
Witchdoctor:	2	4	3	4	3	3	3	4	2	4	2

Regeneration

	Common	Desert	Forest	River	Hill	Mountain	Frozen Waste	Dark	Giant	Two Headed	Trorcs
HTK/Round:	3	4	3	3/2	3	3	4	3	0	1	1

Characteristics

	Common	Desert	Forest	River	Hill	Mountain	Frozen Waste	Dark	Giant	Two Headed	Trorcs
Intelligence:	Low	Very	Ave.	Very	Ave.	Ave.	Ave./Low	Very	Low	Ave/High	Ave/Low
Alignment:	CN/CE	LN/LE	N/LN	LN/LE	NE	CN/CE	NE/CE	LE	CN/CE	CN/CE	CE
Height:	7'-8'	5'-6'	8'-9'	9'	6'-7'	9'-10'	7'-8'	7'-8'	10'-12'	8'-9'	7'-8'
Color:	green-brown	tan-orange	green-brown	brown-grey-tan	brown-grey-tan	red-green-grey brown	grey-white	brown-grey-black	brown-green	brown-grey-tan	red green-yellow brown

Combat

	Common	Desert	Forest	River	Hill	Mountain	Frozen Waste	Dark	Giant	Two Headed	Trorcs
No. Attacks:	3	wpn. only	3	3	3	3	3	wpn. only	2	4	1/3
Damage:	1-4, 1-4, 1-8		2-5, 2-5, 2-8	1-4, 1-4, 1-10	2-5, 2-5, 2-8	2-7, 2-7, 1-12	1-6, 1-6, 1-12		2-7, 2-7	1-6, 1-6, 1-10,1-10	2-12/1-4, 1-4, 2-8
Armor/Shield?	no/no	no/no	yes/no	no/no	no/no	no/no	no/no	yes/yes	no/no	no/no	no/no
Weapons:	Club, Spear	Spear, Bola, Knife	Club, Spear, S. Sword	Net, Trident, Spear, S. Sword	Club, Spear	Spear, Halberd, L. Sword	Spear, Halberd, Battleaxe	Sword	Club, Battleaxe, Lance	Club Staff	Bow and Arrows, Dagger

Natural Abilities (in %)

	Common	Desert	Forest	River	Hill	Mountain	Frozen Waste	Dark	Giant	Two Headed	Trorcs
Camouflage:	70	80	80	95	65	85	90	70	15	10	25
Move Silently:	85	55	45	35	40	35	65	80	25	35	60
Climbing:	60	20	85	25	85	90	40	35	30	25	80
Surprise:	40	90	70	80	25	40	50	50	55	45	60
Setting Traps:	60	20	70	90	80	45	80	90	50	70	35
Tracking:	30	30	55	15	60	65	75	75	45	85	40

Camouflage

The ability the troll possesses to blend in with his sorroundings by standing still, lying, flat on the ground, or hiding in shadows. This percentage only applies to the troll's native habitat; an orange Desert Troll would stand out like a sore thumb in a forest.

Move Silently

The ability of the troll to move quietly through his native terrain. As might be expected, a Mountain Troll used to climbing rocks will not be very silent moving through leaves in a forest.

Climbing

The ability to safely climb things that are native to the troll's area. For example, Forest Trolls climb trees very skillfully, but would not be skilled at climbing the rocky sides of a mountain.

Surprise

The combination of troll's abilities in moving silently and personal camouflage and the self-control to utilize these abilities when actively stalking their prey.

Setting Traps

The ability of a troll to set a snare that will catch and hold prey native to his natural habitat.

Tracking

The troll's skill in tracking prey through his native surroundings.

SHAMAN'S SPELLS				
	Spell Level			
Skill	1	2	3	4
1	1	-	-	-
2	2	-	-	-
3	3	1	-	-
4	3	2	-	-
5	3	3	1	-
6	3	3	2	-
7	3	3	3	1

Shaman, has absolute authority to pick and train the new Shamans. The Shaman trainees are selected from the ranks of mature males and spend the next 10-12 years learning the required skills, spells, and intricacies of respectful worship. When the Tribal Shaman is convinced that a trainee has successfully learned all that can be taught, he is promoted to Shaman. As a Shaman achieves higher skill levels, he gains an additional 1d8 HTK. The Tribal Shaman selects his successor from the Shamans resident in his tribe. In case the Tribal Shaman dies before specifying a successor, the Tribal Chief appoints the new Tribal Shaman. In this case, the Chief can promote an aspiring Shaman from another tribe to be his Tribal Shaman. Unless the new appointee is a skilled and powerful negotiator, he is apt to suffer defections from his staff, leaving him to operate with only trainees for assistance.

Shamans, like the Witchdoctors, have the unquestioned right to offer their services to another tribe at any time. As might be expected, whenever a tribe looses face in inter-tribal combat, many Shamans and Witchdoctors change alliances, often joining the victorious tribe.

The responsibilities of a Shaman include encouraging proper worship from the trolls to insure the favor of the gods, blessing charms and magic weapons, revealing laws passed down by the gods and locating ingredients for healing potions and salves. Though Witchdoctors assist in the latter task, Shamans guard the secret of the ingredients and refuse to allow them to accompany the herb-gathering parties.

Troll leaders are chosen at an annual leadership rite held during the first week of summer. All male trolls wishing to challenge for the position of Tribal Chief fight each other for the privilege of fighting the current Chief. Pairings are drawn by random lot and then the two combatants decide on the type of combat—with weapons or unarmed. No loss of prestige results if hand-to-hand combat is selected. If the pair cannot decide on the type of combat, the Tribal Curate casts tokens and announces the type of fight. The winner of each fight earns a day's rest and recuperation before his next match.

The victor of the challenge group is given a three-day rest and recuperation period to allow complete regeneration. He is also awarded the status of Co-Chief for the three days. The rest of the tribe spends the time in partying and merriment. Then all attention is turned to the main event, a fight to the death for the position of Chief of the tribe.

When the fight is over, the new Chief is blessed by the Tribal Shaman. He then selects his Sub-leaders for the year. Those chosen are obligated to follow the new Chief loyally and not to become a source of discord within the tribe. Then the Sub-leaders are blessed. As a result of superior training and the blessing of the gods, both Chiefs and Sub-leaders gain additional HTK and a lower armor class.

The Sub-leaders are responsible for protecting the Chief, leading the hunting and foraging parties, and enforcing laws passed down by the Shamans. The Chief oversees the activities of the Sub-leaders, serves as chief negotiator with other tribes and parties of humans, insures

J. CLOUSE '82

that all widowed females are rapidly married to the best male (naturally, the Witchdoctors are consulted) and interacts with the Shaman to enforce laws and proper worship of the gods. If a Chief dies during his term of office, the Tribal Curate meditates and fasts for two full days, sacrifices several small animals, casts his tokens, and selects the new Chief from among the Sub-leaders. The Shamans spend this period praying and making sacrifices to the tribal god, asking for the Curate to be granted enough wisdom to make an intelligent choice.

Thus, it is clear that the calm stability of the tribal leadership is in reality a hot-bed of intrigue and double-dealing. It is lucky for the rest of the world that the most intelligent trolls spend much of their time trying to outsmart others of their race.

Tribal Chiefs, Subleaders, Shamans, and Witchdoctors all have more HTK and a different armor class than the average troll.

The following guidelines hold true for all types of trolls:

	HTK	AC adjustment
Chief	+2d8	-2
Sub-leader	+1d8	-1
Shamans	+1d8 per level	+2
Witchdoctors	+1d8 per level	0

LAW, JUSTICE, AND GOVERNMENT

Laws are determined by the Tribal Shaman, who is (or at least claims to be) in direct contact with his god. These laws are enforced by the Chief, and non-compliance results in an automatic death sentence. There are only a few common laws among the trolls. They deal with division of looted treasure, protection of the tribe, and enforcement of religious rituals. Any individual who endangers the tribe, attempts to gain an undue share of the captured treasure, or fails to comply with religious customs and rituals will be summarily sacrificed. There are few transgressors, for all trolls know the entire tribe will rise to purge lawbreakers. The basic laws of the tribe, provide a unifying influence to the chaotic troll society. This concept is important to understand for, were they to exist in a state of complete anarchy, the trolls would quickly be overcome by their enemies.

TROLL VILLAGES AND FORAGING PARTIES

Troll villages show a remarkable similarity throughout all the sub-races, with the natural exclusion of the Common Trolls, who do not build permanent settlements. A troll village rarely has more than 80 members with an organization very similar to that shown below.

1 Chief
1 - 4 Sub-Leaders
6d10 Trolls

1 Witchdoctor (Tribal Curate)
2d6 Assistant Witchdoctors

1 Tribal Shaman
1d4 Shamans
2d4 Shamans in training

Population of the village can be broken down into: 50% males, 45% females, and 5% young. It is likely (65%) that a village will have 10% of its males, a Sub-leader, and an assistant Witchdoctor away on a hunting or foraging expedition. Thus, unless a war party consisting of 80-90% of all the male trolls of a tribe is encountered, the usual group of foraging trolls encountered by adventurers will be 4-10 (2d4+2).

CHILDREARING AND FAMILY LIFE

Trolls regard their females as second class citizens and have relegated them to a subservient role. Females dig for edible roots, and harvest the parches of fungoids, lichens, and mosses that serve as garnishes at most troll tables. They only fight to defend their young and thus have no need for armor or weapons. This inexperience gives female trolls a -1 to all attack rolls. Unlike other races, trolls (except Frozen Waste Trolls) do not gain a bonus for defending themselves or their young.

Female trolls only ovulate three or four times during their 95 year lifespan. The first time this happens, usually at age 15, she will seek-out and mate with the first unattached male she can find. This act, in the eyes of other trolls, joins them into a lifetime pair-bond. Male trolls, once bonded, will be given additional wives by the tribe Chief who is responsible for all unattached females past their first cycle. Mature females must be owned and cared for; thus new widows are quickly joined with new mates. The bond-wife, however new and inexperienced, has complete authority over all other wives in the household.

Three months after mating, the female lays her 3 or 4 eggs in suitable spots (traditionally large holes covered by dirt and a boulder or rock to protect it from predators). When an egg hatches, the young troll must break free of his "tomb". Those too weak to tunnel out are allowed to die, thereby assuring survival of the fittest. After escaping, the young make their way (it is hypothesized by smell) to their mother, who accepts them nonchalantly. Males appear not to take much notice or pay attention to the family's new addition. The young are not nursed since they are fully capable of eating normal troll fare from birth. Within a week, their regenerative abilities appear, and troll young soon gain adequate strength to pursue activities as dictated by their sex. Within a year, they are fully mature.

COMMON TROLLS vary slightly from the norm, primarily as a result of their wandering nature. After the female lays her eggs, she and her mate remain in the area until the eggs hatch and mature adequately to permit moving on. In winter months, this may necessitate their finding a cave or similar lodging to weather the worst of the storms.

FOREST TROLLS typically bury their eggs in the ground, covering them with fallen trees for protection, preferring dark, dank places where predators seldom wander. Unlike other sub-races, regenerative abilities appear within 3-4 days of hatching

RIVER TROLLS cannot bury the eggs underwater since gills develop about 6 weeks after hatching; the same period of time is required for their regenerative abilities to develop. The land is seen as hostile, so River Trolls leave their eggs in underwater homes of Giant Beavers. The Beavers accept the eggs and tend them until the baby troll hatches. At this time, the female and her mate retrieve their offspring and move to a hidden spot along the riverbank, which serves as their home until the young troll has developed its gills. This period is very important to the young troll, for he is taught basic skills in swimming, camouflage, and foraging by his father.

DESERT TROLLS bury their eggs in the hot sands of the desert. Upon hatching, the young troll must survive long enough to dig to the surface (some four feet above him) and then locate one of the hidden entrances to the underground complexes that will be his home. Desert Troll regenerative powers take approximately three months to develop. Any obviously weak or deformed young are immediately killed, for in the harsh desert environment, they would be a constant drain on the tribe's resources.

FROZEN WASTE TROLLS: Because the ground is frozen most of the year, Frozen Waste Troll child-rearing techniques vary greatly from the norm. In their caverns, they carefully prepare nest of twigs, scraps of cloth, leather and furs. The females, after laying their egg, will actually warm them with their bodies until they hatch. These young trolls mature slowly, gaining full strength after 5 months; though their regenerative abilities appear within a week. Unlike other sub-races, the young do not participate in normal activity for the first year of life. They stay close to the mother for that time, until their thick layer of water-retaining body fat has developed. Only then are they allowed to participate in adult activities. Of all the troll sub-races, only Frozen Waste Trolls appear to show any familial attachments. Males receive an attack bonus of +1 if their females or young are endangered, and females receive a bonus of +3 if their offspring or eggs are threatened.

HILL TROLLS bury their eggs in Forest Troll fashion. The regenerative abilities of the young, however, do not appear for 3-4 weeks. In recent years, many have been born without this ability, thus attributing greatly to the gradual extinction of the sub-race; only 20% of all newborn survive. No explanation has been found for this steady decline, although some claim that the Hill Trolls have ceased proper worship of their god and are being punished for their perfidy.

FOOD AND CLOTHING

Although diet varies due to environment and inclination, food items common to the diet of all trolls are: small and large animals, large flightless birds, roots, plants, lichens, mosses, and fungoids that grow in caves and forests.

Clothing is shunned by most trolls for they have thick hides and do not require the extra protection. It is worn primarily by those trolls who live in the vicinity of civilization and have fallen under its influence. Giant Trolls, in an imitation of true Giants, and Frozen Waste Trolls, living in frigid areas, wear hides and furs for warmth.

COMMON TROLLS have the greatest range of diet, for their wandering takes them across a wide variety of terrain. They eat small animals (squirrels and rabbits), as well as larger game (wild boar, deer, bear). Skins and furs of large animals are cured and traded to other forest dwellers in exchange for weapons. Common Trolls often raid farms, stealing eggs, chicken, goats, and sheep (for which they have a special fondness). Food is eaten raw, with the bloody organs reserved for the males and the less preferred portions left to the females. Stolen goats are herded by these wandering bands, for goat's milk is considered a nutrient of the gods. When this animal finally dies, it is burned, not eaten. The horns, revered as magical, are carved into charms and trinkets to ward off the influence of hostile spirits.

FOREST TROLLS have a wide variety of food animals to choose from. They prefer to hunt small game using traps that are checked several times a day. Adept tree climbers, Forest Trolls also steal eggs from bird's nests (along with any young fledglings that they can find) and consume them with great relish. Although they are not adept fishermen, they do enjoy fish and will often trade healing potions and salves for this delicacy. Since they shun clothing, the skins of the animals they trap are utilized as a lining for their sleeping nests. These large nests are also made with leaves, twigs, and a variety of mosses and grasses.

RIVER TROLLS have evolved subsisting on a diet of fish, lichen, grasses, and algae. The large variety of water plants which coat the rocks and boulders of the river bottom and banks are greatly relished. River Trolls are usually found where fish are plentiful, for they trap fish and breed them in great caverns sealed off with netting. The excess fish are traded to land dwellers (both human and troll). Like most other trolls, they have a predilection for a variety of bitter roots, and will occasionally travel to the darkest corners of forests to harvest them. Those who do not live in the vicinity of a forest often establish small trading posts to attract wandering Common Trolls to whom they pay exorbitant prices (in fish, gems, and jewelry) for these roots.

MOUNTAIN TROLLS, as noted above, hunt by night. They seek out large predators (bears, lions, or mountain cats), for they enjoy the fight as much as the food. Small game is left untouched for they consider it beneath them to hunt insignificant animals.

After the battle, the bloody organs are given to the Chief and Shaman, while the remaining parts are distributed among the rest of the tribe. Naturally, the better portions go to the males, the remainder to the females. Furs and hides are cured and serve as bedrolls and ceremonial cloaks for the Shamans. Excess furs are traded for weapons and other items—trinkets, amulets, and charms to ward off evil spirits. Mountain Trolls also love roots and fungoids and no meal is eaten without them. Their females spend copious amounts of time harvesting bitter roots for consumption and use as trade goods.

FROZEN WASTE TROLLS, despite their harsh environment, have no shortage of food. A wide variety of game abounds in the snow covered lands, with both land and sea animals providing plentiful hunting. Bears, snow foxes, ice hounds, snow leopards, ice worms, artic hares, seals, walrus, and arctic owls are the mainstays of their diet. This is augmented by the roots and other produce they can barter for.

DESERT TROLLS have three major food sources: snakes, cacus, and captured goods. Snakes, plentiful on the surface, are trapped and raised beneath the burning sands in great caverns. Snake meat, the staple of their diet, is eaten raw or boiled in great cauldrons with pieces of small game and large chunks of bitter cactus. Cactus leaves are harvested and small game is hunted on a daily basis to augment and give variety to the diet. Monthly forays into the lands fringing the deserts bring larger game and an exchange of trade goods with other trolls. The most commonly traded items are tanned snake skins, captured trade goods, and slaves.

DARK TROLLS, living almost exclusively underground, have adapted their dietary habits to utilize the potential food sources found in subterranean lairs. The meat of Carrion Crawlers, Giant Rats, and Rust Monsters is their most common fare. Rust Monsters are the only animal specifically bred for food. With one exception, all food is consumed raw; crawler meat is cooked into a thick greasy soup flavored with a variety of fungoids and mosses typically found in the caverns beneath the ground. The very smell of this concoction is enough to appall even the most hardened adventurers, though the trolls seem quite immune to the effects of either the soup or the stench.

TROLL GODS AND RITUALS

There are four known dieties worshipped by the various troll races.

YARGNARRAL

AC: -3
HTK: 275
Stats: 19, 27/24, 19/24, 25, 20, 12

Yargnarral is a large (11' tall), Two Headed Troll of grey-green coloration, the spawn of a Frozen Waste female and the god Tarnargle. Though no real proof exists to substantiate the legend, it is said that Tarnargle, while battling Toreg Rock Carver (the Dwarven diety), was driven into the Frozen Wastelands. There, he was entombed alive in a mountain of ice, unable to either free himself—or to die. Many thousands of years later, a Frozen Waste female, experiencing her first cycle and having no unattached males to turn to, journeyed to a nearby settlement. Seeking refuge for the night, she found the entombed god in an icy cavern. In the heat of her mating frenzy, she spent two weeks clawing at the ice to free him, sensing somehow that he still lived. In gratitude, the god consented to mate with her. Though she was bereft of a life-mate, she was content, receiving many gifts and gems from Targnargle.

Yargnarral, the offspring of this union, became leader of the trolls and spent 300 years living in the Frozen Wastes. He was a Shaman/Witchdoctor of great power, with innate magical powers. He was able to use his Cone of Ice breath weapon once every three turns, delivering a Blast of Cold inflicting 10d20 points of damage. He could also cast an Ice Storm three times a day, producing great boulders of ice falling from the sky, delivering 10d8 points of damage on everyone within a 100' radius from the center of the spell.

Following the great battle in which he victoriously led his people against an invasion by the Southern Orcs, he was called to serve his father for a period of 1,000 years. His people, grieving for their great leader began to offer sacrifices to him. Upon completion of his 1,000 years servitude, he was so powerful that he was allowed a place in the pantheon. He is highly protective of his people (there is a 20% chance that he will hear the call of any troll engaged in battle against a formidable foe, sending assistance in the

form of two great Ice Toads). Yargnarral has forbidden his worshippers to perform sacrifices to him, except in the form of exterminating his hated foe, the Orcs.

TARGNARGLE

AC:	1
HTK:	260
Stats:	25, 23, 20,
	22, 23, 14

Targnargle is the most commonly worshipped of the troll dieties. He is a creature of immense strength and stamina created by a Demon Prince. Resembling the trolls of old, he quickly gained their trust, led them in victorious battles against the other dark races, and demanded worship in bloody sacrifice. Targnargle, Lawful Evil in alignment, requires unfailing subservience from his worshippers. Sacrifices, required during the first three nights of the new moon consist of disembowling live victims, eating their organs, and hanging the bodies from trees or posts to be ravaged by predators and birds of prey.

Tarnargle's Shamans have the power once per month to rupture the soft organs in a living individual. This is known among trolls as the Bloodless Sacrifice, and is reserved to punish trolls who violate common troll law and to deal with enemy spell casters. Many Shamans will then eat the brains of the victim of a Bloodless Sacrifice, believing they gain the powers of their victims.

SZKARNADLE

AC:	0
HTK:	200
Stats:	21, 19, 19,
	24, 23, 08

Oldest of the troll gods, Szkarnardle serves the forces of the powerful, almost forgotten elder gods. Some legends state that Szkarnardle created the trolls to wreak revenge on humanity for the banishment of the elder gods. Weekly sacrifices of humanoids are required to satisfy his blood-lust. Sacrifice is made by draining the victims' blood, drinking the blood, and then scattering the body parts to animals of prey. Worship of Szkarnardle, like the elder gods, is rapidly becoming a thing of the past among the trolls.

15

LIRABYTH
(GODDESS OF TROLLS)

AC: -5
HTK: 377
Stats: 20, 22, 20,
25, 22, 06
(21 to trolls)

Lirabyth appears as a huge four-winged snake with the head of a very plain woman. She is covered with glistening green scales, but derives her low armor class from her great dexterity and speed (she flies at 128" per round). She has a 67% magic resistance and her scales act as a Ring of Spell Turning. She normally has just one attack, a lightning-fast strike with her tail that does 10d10 points of damage. She can summon and control 10d100 snakes; they will appear whenever she wants them and will attempt to carry out her wishes until they are killed. Once Lirabyth has instructed them, she is free to proceed on to other tasks.

If any creatures manages to catch her up in the air, she can spit a deadly poison at her pursuers. The poison stream is three inches wide and travels 150'. All struck must save vs. poison at -5 or be immediately paralyzed and take 10d8 HTK damage from the caustic acid base in the poison; those that save will be blinded for 1-4 rounds and take half damage.

Lirabyth loves the trolls, for they find her beautiful. She prefers her sacrifices to come from the other snake-hating dark races. She draws much energy from the fear emitted by victims sacrificed at the Snake Gardens. Every 200 years, when she appears on the material plane, the worshipping trolls always have 500+ victims to sacrifice to her. In return, she allows her Troll Shamans (of level 3 and above) to ask her for assistance three times a year. This keeps her in constant contact with and allows her to command the trolls, her chosen creatures.

ILLNESS AND HEALING

Trolls are extremely hardy and seldom experience illness or disease, and are apparently immune to even the most virulent plagues to which humans are prone. There are two diseases, however, that affect them. One, a disease of the joints, causes debilitating and searing pain, eventually causing paralysis. The other disease attacks the mind, causing hallucinations, derangement, and eventual death.

Due to these diseases, troll Shamans began to experiment with the production of healing potions; many of them died from natural poisons before any discoveries were made. In the centuries that have elapsed since the troll migrations, this knowledge and skill has been lost to all but the Forest, River, and Mountain Trolls, who now manufacture potions and salves for the other troll subraces and the rest of the Dark Folk. Naturally, they are able to demand a very high price for these items.

TRADES AND CRAFTS

Trolls, as a race, have no specialized skills other than mining. Only the Dark Trolls have any smithing skills, so common utensils, such as pots, knives, weapons, and armament are traded for or stolen. One talent, shared by all the subraces, is the troll skill in carving small, intricate, life-like figurines from bone. Many of those carvings find their way to human cities and demand a high price.

RIVER TROLLS have learned to weave baskets from reeds found along the river banks and use them to collect and move the smaller debris in the river near their homes. Excess baskets are sold, thus most troll households have one or more of these containers for storing the family's possessions. River Trolls also trap fish, breeding them in gigantic underwater caves closed off with nets. In fish-poor areas, the River Trolls often become quite wealthy, selling fish to the land-dwellers (both human and other Dark Folk).

DARK TROLLS are the only subrace among the trolls to possess skills in weapon making. Dark Troll weaponsmiths are not as proficient as dwarven smiths, but are at least as good as human smiths. Similar to dwarven smiths, Dark Trolls align their normal weapons to their race, giving them an effective +1 to hit when wielded by a troll. In addition, each weapon is specifically crafted and specifically aligned for its new owner.

Troll Witchdoctors and Shamans perform ancient, lengthly rituals during the preparation of the weapon. These include a bloodletting of the future owner onto the blade of the sword, while being hammered, in order to imbue the sword with intelligence, a purpose, or special properties. Wielded by their owners, the Dark Troll swords become truly awesome weapons. Dark Trolls can manufacture magical swords with up to a +3 attack bonus. Many different weapons are manufactured for other trolls, but these are usually not magical.

RACE RELATIONS

Trolls fear no other creature. Their great size and strength make them a formidable opponent, even discounting their regenerative abilities. Equally hardy or strong races, lacking the regenerative ability simply cannot contend with the trolls, and take great care not to place themselves in a position of having to do so. Since trolls never bluff (they lack the patience and the wisdom to conceal their true feelings) all the other races know the troll's attitude toward them.

Trolls dislike the other Dark Races, considering them weak and cowardly. They do have a grudging respect for Gnolls, who at least appear to exhibit courage, and have compatible ideas regarding sacrifice. However, they are not friendly with Gnolls, for the trolls are intolerant of the superior attitude of the Gnolls. Occasionally, skirmishes break out between the two races when trading is underway, usually instigated by the boastful attitude of the Gnolls.

Kobolds are disregarded completely, except when

dinner and sacrificial victims are needed. Occasionally, Kobolds are enslaved and bred for labor; after their useful period is over, they are killed in sacrifice.

Orcs, considered to be worthless even as sacrificial victims, are exterminated mercilessly. The Orc predeliction for capturing trolls (usually the disease-weakened ones, as the trolls are fond of saying) and using them as a regenerating food supply is viewed very dimly by trolls.

Goblins are rated much as Kobolds, that is, beneath contempt. Hobgoblins are seen as little more than overgrown Goblins, much to the irritation of the Hobgoblins who seek out every opportunity to wage war and skirmish against the trolls. Ogres are accorded a grudging respect because of their equitable strength, though their stupidity is a subject of much mirth and merriment.

Humans are accorded the position of a special adversary. Though a much weaker race, humans have a nasty habit of striking the trolls when least expected. The highest achievement a troll can make is to infiltrate a human settlement and return with a living hostage. The hostage is then presented to the Chief as a gift, bringing much honor to the troll that captured him. Forest and River Trolls, continually interacting with humans, have abandoned this practice, but even they do not truly trust or like humans. Trolls do not understand the human style of government, but are very aware that quite often pacts between trolls and humans have been casually broken.

MOUNTAIN TROLLS are particularly hostile toward Dwarves and Gnomes. with whom they vie for living space. They will often wage war—or at least frequent invasions—with enslavement in mind. This, of course, is not tolerated by the Dwarves, to whom enslavement is anathema, and an almost constant state of war exist between the two races whenever they are within a short distance of each other.

HILL TROLLS, quickly fading from the face of the earth, are very fond of Halflings, especially when roasted over a slow fire. If there is a Halfling settlement within a two week journey, the Hill Trolls will make regular raids into the settlement. Fearing the extremely accurate aim of the Halfling archers, the trolls appear at night to capture late night stragglers. Though suffering no real injury from the volley of arrows, trolls often find themselves disabled by the sheer number of shafts protuding from their bodies, and the resultant similarity to porcupines offends their sense of dignity.

INTER - TRIBAL RELATIONS

As the early trolls spread over the land and adapted to their new surroundings, they no longer considered themselves to be a unified race. Their differing life styles created rifts among the divergent groups and inter-group skirmishes became more and more common.

Trolls of differing subraces will hurl taunts and jeers at each other. If two large war parties meet, their leaders will often (70%) engage in battle. The battle, not usually fought to the death, ends when one party's leader is disarmed or badly wounded. At this point, the victor claims the loser's sword (or other weapon) as his prize, and the shamed party is driven off amidst jeers. The claimed weapon is displayed in a prominent place in the victor's tribe, and can be regained only by a ransom in the form of gems, jewelry, slaves, healing potions, goats, or other herd animals.

Until the weapon is reclaimed, the loser's entire tribe is shamed, and must send all their females to the victor's tribe to serve as slaves. A tribe that refuses to do this will be mercilessly exterminated by all other troll tribes in the area. Those who cannot find a way to redeem the weapon (and

incidentally their females) become outcasts and must turn to a life of roving.

COMMON TROLLS love to challenge other groups of trolls. They have a unique attitude regarding these challenge matches; if their leader is bested, they immediately elect a new leader and demand a new trial by combat, stating that the old chief was obviously inept. This tactic usually results in a great troll-vs.-troll melee that decimates both parties. As a result, most troll subraces will not allow themselves to be challenged by Common Trolls.

When threatened by a common enemy, all the troll subraces, despite their many differences, will unite under the rulership of an Overlord. The Overlord is chosen from the greatest troll Chieftans by the Tribal Shamans, who spend two days fasting, meditating, and communing with the gods. Trolls can thus present a solid front to their enemies for a limited number of years. Several Overlords have attempted to maintain control over such a Nation of Trolls, but none have been successful. When the battle was over, or the threat eradicated, the varying subraces would once again become quarrelsome and uncooperative.

SLAVERY

Trolls occasionally take slaves to perform difficult tasks, especially when new tunnels are under construction. There are communal slaves in every tribe, but only a small number are kept, thus avoiding the threat of a slave uprising. When a large number of slaves are taken during a raid, they are held captive only long enough to be "tamed". The "taming" involves torture, hard work, and abuse for as long as any rebelliousness shows itself. Slavers regularly visit Mountain and Desert Troll villages; they pay high prices for Troll-tamed prisoners.

MAGIC ITEMS

Trolls, unlike the humans, have only a few magic items. Those they possess are produced by the Witchdoctors (or stolen). Requiring a great expenditure of power, the production of magic implements leaves the Witchdoctor vulnerable for long periods of time; thus accounting for the paucity of magic items. Trolls are distrustful of magic in general, with the exception of items produced by the Witchdoctors or the Dark Trolls. However, those trolls that cannot detect magic, will use any weapon or wear any trinket that pleases them, unaware of any magical properties inherent in the item. Here is a partial list of magic items that troll Witchdoctors can make.

PROTECTION CHARMS, carved from animal and human bones, are fashioned by the trolls, blessed and enchanted by Witchdoctors, and implanted under the skin. Some offer protection against spells, (i.e. fire, acid, breath weapon attacks, etc.), giving a +1 to the save of an individual with such a charm. Only one such implant is possible at one time and will not work for non-trolls.

CHARMS OF COMMAND, carved from the bones of an aquatic animal by River Troll Shamans and implanted under the skin like a Protection Charm, will allow the wearer to communicate with similar aquatic animals (i.e., beavers, otters, seals, badgers). The possessor of such a charm will also be able to control the animal to a limited extent (lowers the animal's save by -4). These charms are useable by non-trolls, but only if they already understand Trollish.

THE CLAY JARS, created by the Forest Troll Witchdoctors, are eagerly sought by all trolls. Any item placed in one of these jars will always remain fresh and untainted. Used to store healing herbs and food for long periods, these jars are in great demand among humans. No troll will ever sell or voluntarily part with a Clay Jar. Any troll discovering a non-troll in possession of a Clay Jar will attempt to slay the owner and recover the Jar.

ARTIFACTS

Although magic is scarce, the trolls possess a number of highly valued artifacts, given them by their gods. Most revered are the following:

THE RED CLAW is a mummified troll hand with a red stain in the form of a goat covering the back of the hand. The Claw's origin is unknown, but is usually attributed to the time of the elder gods. Powers granted by the claw allow its bearer to perform as a fighter at twice his actual level of effectiveness, properly weild any weapon, enjoy an AC two steps lower than normal, and add +2 to all saving throws. It is currently in the possession of one of the Mountain Troll Shamans. Since his acquisition of the artifact, he has inexplicably grown a third arm and his skin has begun to show signs of red splotching.

THE GREAT ICE SPEAR, apparently composed of ice that will not melt, will, when hurled, cause a great ice storm around the spot where it strikes the ground. Fist-sized hail pounds the ground within a 100 yard radius inflicting 10d6 HTK of damage each round for 1-6 rounds. The Spear is reputed to allow the wielder to travel to the Elemental Plane of Water and, once there, impress into his service 1d4 Water Elementals for a period of 1d10 days. This can be done once per year. Its current owner, a Frozen Waste Chieftan, is unaware that the Spear powers itself on the endurance or constitution of the weilder, leeching ½ point per month until 9 is reached. At that time, the Spear will stop functioning, until claimed by a new owner. The spear will work for any non-troll who activates it by dipping it in the blood of a freshly killed (within 15 minutes) White Dragon.

THE MIRROR OF LOCATION is a crude mirror of polished metal, set in a copper frame and is highly valued among Trolls. It is currently in the possession of one of the Hill Troll Shamans who activates it by a command word, written in ancient Trollish, inscribed on the back of the frame. The the viewer merely has to specify a creature, and the mirror will show him the location of the nearest member of the requested type (e.g. Halfling, Kobold, Unicorn, etc.). The mirror will not show the location of a specific individual (i.e., Red Nose Treetrunk, the local Witchdoctor). Needless to say, the Hill Trolls value this artifact greatly; with its help, they have been able to enjoy many tasty Halfling stews and roasts in the past few years.

THE PORTABLE WELL, resembling a tattered and torn rag, is the pride and joy of the Desert Trolls. They recovered it, at great expense, from the tomb of a powerful Forest Troll Shaman. After stealing the artifact, the party headed homeward, but, in the course of a few days, every member of the raiding party fell ill from some unknown disease and died. The lone survivor, a female who had not taken part in the desecration of the grave, buried the dead and faithfully carried it to her tribe. Javvo Snakeskinner, for this act was given the honorary position of Co-Chief for the rest of her days; the only female troll to ever achieve this elevated rank.

When the tattered cloth is folded in four, laid on the ground and carefully reopened, it becomes a well, complete with a handle, crank, and bucket. This Well provides an endless supply of pure, cool water. When the Well is no longer needed, one merely detaches the bucket from the rope, and it entirely disappears, leaving a crumpled rag on the ground in its place. No activating word is needed to operate it, just the proper method of folding and unfolding the cloth.

THE SNARE ROPES OF THE ELDER TROLLS are lengths of rope woven from the hair of different animals. Originally, there were nine such ropes, but currently only the location of the Rabbit, Deer, Bear, and Lion Ropes are known. When a Rope is thrown to the ground and the command word spoken, it forms into a snare that will trap the animal from whose fur it is made. The snare will activate itself only if the correct animal passes over it; when this happens, its victim is completely ensnared and cannot escape. When another command word is spoken, the Snare Rope will go limp, allowing the creature to be released.

CONCLUSION

Trolls are a fierce, vigorous race. Though humans are occasionally captured for use as slaves, other dark folk are treated with less respect and are often used as food or sacrificial offerings. Some troll sub-species, notably River and Forest Trolls, are moving closer and closer toward civilized attitudes and cooperation with humans. As time goes on, it is hoped that a true spirit of trust between the races will alleviate the barbaric ways of the troll.

In the meantime, if you must travel in the Troll's sphere of influence, try and be practical. Always take along a few extra sheep and goats, trinkets, common implements, and a few weapons as gifts for any trolls you might meet. Proving yourself to be a valuable asset to them may be the only way to preserve your life.

THE TROLL ULTIMATUM

AUTHOR'S NOTE

This adventure was designed for a party of 6 to 8 characters of 5th through 8th levels of ability with at least three magic items specifically designed to neutralize Trolls.

This adventure was designed to be played on the continent of Mamaryl, but can be easily dropped into your campaign by doing the following:

1. The city of Jovian Falls must be placed in a river large enough to support commerce;

2. Trolls must be introduced into the nearby waterways and forests;

3. The Troll Caverns can be placed under any mountain 10-15 miles from Jovian Falls;

4. Locate the Troll Temple in an uninhabited area 30-40 miles from the town. (Distances for (3) and (4) are relative and may be changed to suit your needs.)

You will also note that little specific detail has been filled in for the town of Jovian Falls. You may populate the town according to the theme of your campaign or you may use the random building size/business charts provided with the adventure. A history of Jovian Falls can be found in "Adventure: Part One."

INTRODUCTION
(to be read to the players)

Your hearty, hardy, and fearless group of adventurers has just arrived in the town of Jovian Falls (for whatever reason), and, settling in at the Shady Tree Inn, you ask about places of local interest. You are told of the Haunted Forest, the Troll Apothecary (where you can purchase both common and very rare magical components), the Snake Gardens, the Rune Stone, the Wishing Well, the Troll Totems, and the Troll Museum. After careful (though brief) consideration, you decide on a night of celebrations and general carousing, retiring late that night to your rooms. Arising in the morning, you discover that the week of relaxation and rest that had been envisioned is not to be, for the innkeeper announces that the Trolls have placed the town under seige. Dashing out into the streets, you find no evidence of a seige, by Trolls, or anyone else, and you put down the innkeeper's excitement to lunacy.

During breakfast, however, a military escort arrives and you are informed that the Duke desires you to attend him at once—and from the look of the guards, it seems prudent not to argue.

Duke Borin, ruler of Jovian Falls, greets you, and it is obvious that your reputation (be it fair or foul) has preceeded you, for the Duke knows several of your exploits. He tells you the relations between the town of Jovian Falls and the River and Forest Troll populations in the area have been quite good for many years. Various treaties and pacts, insuring peace for all, have been signed, but were recently broken by foreign Trolls, and passage to Jovian Falls is no longer secure nor safe.

Both the Duke and Ia Uprooter, the Chief of the Jovian River Trolls were upset by this unexpected turn of events after such a long time of peace, and it was decided that a party of Trolls and men, led by Ia Uprooter and Louis Bronwyn (cousin to Duke Borin) would leave to

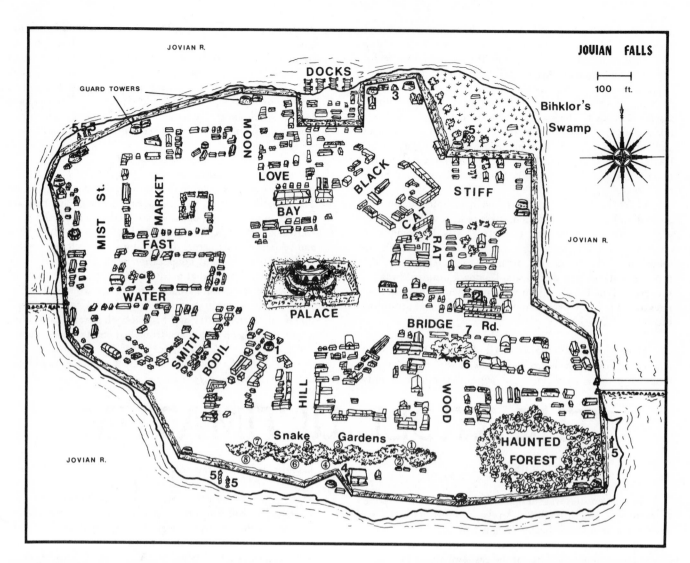

search out the cause of the problem. They left two weeks ago to search out the leader of the Black Wyvern Mountain Trolls and have not been heard of since.

He further informs you that early this morning, a group of 15 Frozen Waste Trolls appeared before the main entrance to Jovian Falls, demanding to speak with the Duke. When granted an audience, they informed the Duke that most of Ia and Louis' party (including Ia and Louis) had been captured. The party will be held as hostages (the Trolls refused to say by whom) and overland and river travel will not be permitted unless the Duke pays a tribute of a quarter of a million gold pieces in ransom or returns to the Trolls their two religious artifacts, known as the Bronze Mask and Orb.

The Troll delegation has given the Duke 24 hours to respond to their demand in writing. If he is willing to accede to their demands, they will give him 30 days in which to raise the funds or deliver the Mask and Orb. At the end of the thirty days, if their demand is not met, their armies will flatten the town.

Having relied too long on the goodwill of the Trolls to ensure peace in the area, the Duke finds himself without extra troops to mount a campaign and still protect the town. Further, the Duke does not have a quarter of a million gold pieces, nor is he in a position to raise that amount. Alternately, he doesn't have—or know anything

about—the Bronze Mask and Orb, and therefore cannot give them up. To buy time, however, he is willing to promise delivery of one or the other within the 30 day limit in order to buy time. In the meantime, he is impressing all competent adventurers currently in town into the Dukal Militia.

Having heard of your reputations, he feels that he can make the best use of your talents by giving you a free hand —raise the money by whatever means at your disposal (slay a Dragon and steal its hoard, dig up some buried treasure, etc.) or locate the Bronze Mask and Orb. If you prove successful, he tells you, the court Herald will broadcast your names throughout the land and neighboring kingdoms and you will be known as the saviours of Jovian Falls, knighted, and honored as heroes.

FOR THE DM: If the party is unwilling to accept the Duke's offer, they will be thrown into the dungeons and the adventure is at an end. If they accept his "offer" and then try to run out on the Duke, they will discover that their "cowardice" and "treachery" are known wherever they go, and will be hunted down and jailed at first opportunity!

The Duke has no information regarding the Bronze Mask and Orb. He has never heard of them. If questioned by the party, he will tell them the following:

1. There is a Sage in town, Arilan the Not-so-Tall, who has specialized in Troll History and Mythology. Perhaps he might be able to throw light on the matter.

2. There is a Troll Museum within the city walls, containing various Troll Artifacts found in the area when it was settled by humans. Arilan runs the Museum.

3. There is a Snake Garden near the Museum tended now by some Druids who might have some information about the Troll items.

4. There are several Totems in the nearby region which are believed to be Trollish in origin.

After relating the information, the Duke will withdraw, for he has several other parties to induct. He wishes you well and hopes you will return with some solution to the problem—for if you do not, the town of Jovian Falls will in all likelihood fall to the hordes of Trolls.

FOR THE DM
BACKGROUND INFORMATION

The basis for the events leading to this adventure is found in history. Prior to settlement by humans, the island was the sacred holy ground of the Trolls. The Snake Gardens, a popular attraction in Jovian Falls, is in reality the sacrificial altar of the Trolls for the demon snake goddess they worship.

When the humans settled the island and drove out the Trolls, they did not discover the purpose of the Gardens, and they have existed unchanged to this day, carefully tended by Druids. All has gone well for a very long time, but now the two hundred year cycle marking the visitation of the goddess is at hand. The Trolls fear the goddess' ire if she discovers that not only have they been ousted from the island, but have lost the two great artifacts she bestowed upon them—the Bronze Mask and Orb.

In an effort to recover the artifacts that would allow them to consecrate another site to their goddess, the Trolls have evolved a plan to force the humans who caused this trouble to be their salvation. To achieve this, they began to harass trade between Jovian Falls and the outside world. When the Duke sent out a small party led by his cousin and the River Troll Chieftain to discover the cause of the harassment, it was captured and the party held prisoner. The Trolls, under the direction of their patriarch, Arksnout, cut off all trade to and from Jovian Falls, and then sent an ultimatum to the Duke: Either pay a ransom of a quarter of a million gold pieces or return the Bronze Mask and Orb within 30 days, or be annihilated by the powerful Troll army. Knowing full well that the Duke did not have the access to such a great sum, they reasoned that he would attempt to located the artifacts instead. Preparing for the confrontation, an army of more than 1,000 Trolls has gathered north of the Troll Cavern. Under the leadership of Osgoth-Sogoth, a Two Headed Troll, the army is patiently waiting for Arksnout's Command to attack the town of Jovian Falls.

While locating the artifacts is relatively simple, the adventure is not. Once the artifacts are returned, the party will discover (and not until then!) that unless they can regain the artifacts, they will be slain by the goddess when she appears in 30 days time for having driven the Trolls from the island and denied them access to their sacrificial altar. Their only hope of salvation, is to recover the artifacts from the Trolls in time.

Should the party in some way manage to pay the monetary ransom, they will still be faced with the same problem (except that they may not know it) plus an attack from the Trolls, who will decimate the city in an effort to —at least, in part—pacify their goddess.

The properties of the Bronze Mask and Orb (when worn and held by the same person) are as follows:

1. They allow the wielder to consecrate ground to the goddess to serve as a new altar.

2. They act as a gate which allows the goddess to travel to this plane. Note that they do not have to be held for this power to function, the Snake Goddess can focus on and gate to only one of the items if they are not in the possession of the same person.

3. They allow the user to communicate directly with the goddess. Treat this ability as a Commune spell, usable only once a month.

4. They allow the user to control and speak with all snakes, and speak Trollish.

5. They allow the user to cast Neutralize Poison three times a day.

6. They allow the user to cast Pyrotechnics four times a day.

7. They allow the user to cast a Spectral Force spell once a day.

8. They will cause the user to become Chaotic Evil in alignment if a saving throw at -4 is not made: if made, it will still force the alignment of the user one step closer to Chaotic Evil.

9. They will cause the possessor to slowly turn into a Dark Troll (over a period of about 6 months).

10. Each use will drain ¼ point of intelligence from the user to a minimum of 6.

11. They will allow the user to cast the spell Sticks to Snakes three times a day.

12. They are the only means whereby the goddess can be slain. In order to accomplish this, the goddess must be on this plane and the possessor must destroy the artifacts (they can be easily smashed) in her presence (within 100 feet).

DM NOTE: This information can be obtained only from the Sage after the artifacts are returned to the Trolls.

FOR THE DM ONLY: Listed below are the various points of interest that were pointed out to the party on their arrival in the town or by the Duke. They can serve as beginning points for the adventure. Allow the group to decide for themselves, by a method of trial and error, what they wish to do and how they wish to go about their task.

The party at this point has four choices:

1. Leave the area without helping, or refuse to help and be imprisoned. (see above)

2. Search the countryside for treasure. If they choose this option, roll an encounter once per hour, with a 15% chance of an unusual encounter of your choice—5% chance to discover the Troll Caverns daily (after the first two days). If they head directly for the Black Wyvern Mountains south of town, give them a 20% daily chance to locate the Troll Caverns.

3. Follow the courier back when they obtain the Duke's message and try to eliminate the Troll leaders and/or discover more of the plot.

4. Visit places in town attempting to get more information about Trolls and perhaps locate the artifacts. If they do not figure out how the teleport patterns work, allow them to track the messengers if they try to do it later.

THE FLOW OF THE ADVENTURE

Part One of the adventure consists of the arrival of the party in Jovian Falls, their induction into the Duke's service, and their initial travels through the town in search of a starting place. As stated before, the party has been given a number of clues which should allow them to discover the artifacts and the teleport system.

Part Two of the adventure begins when the party discovers the Troll Caverns, finds the massed Troll Army, their leaders, the Hidden Temple, and in the Temple, the Tome which describes the uses of the artifacts.

Part Three of the adventure begins when the party finds the artifacts. (Please note that it is not impossible that the party will discover the artifacts before starting or completing part two of the adventure.) Once the artifacts

are found, duly turned over to the Duke, and presented to the Trolls, an excited Sage Arilan will arrive in court. He will inform the Duke and the party members that it was indeed fortunate that the artifacts were discovered, for he has discovered further information relating to them. It seems that the two hundred year cycle of the demon snake goddess' visitation is about to occur. When the goddess discovers that the Trolls have been driven from the island, she will undoubtedly decimate Jovian Falls to the last man. Only by destroying the artifact in the goddess' presence (within 100 feet) could they hope to kill the goddess, thereby saving Jovian Falls.

This announcement should immediately propel the party to Part Two of the adventure (perhaps for the first time) to recapture the artifacts in time to save Jovian Falls. By the time the party starts after the artifacts, the Trolls with the Bronze Mask and the Orb will have disappeared into the forests. Their trail, if followed, will lead to the Troll Caverns. By the time the party reaches the Temple, the Bronze Mask and Orb will be safely stashed in the treasure vault.

ADVENTURE PART ONE
IMPORTANT LOCATIONS IN JOVIAN FALLS

Should the party decide to confer with the Sage mentioned by the Duke, they will be directed to the house of Arilan the Not-so-Tall (7), a Sage who has spent most of his long life in the study of things Trollian. He is a loquacious, absentminded type of fellow, who is somewhat given to rambling.

Upon learning that his visitors are newcomers to Jovian Falls, he will insist upon giving them a lecture on local history, and will then wax eloquent on his favorite subject —Trolls. Unfortunately, he is unable to shed any light upon the nature of the Bronze Mask and Orb, though he promises to begin researching immediately. (Unfortunately, this research will take more time than the party has—in fact it will not be completed until the artifacts have been returned to the Trolls.) If called upon, he will describe each of the items to be found in the museum (see below).

HISTORY OF JOVIAN FALLS

The unnamed island where the town of Jovian Falls now stands was discovered by a large party of trappers looking for the headwaters of the Jovian River about two hundred years ago. Nearly three quarters of a mile south of the island, river travel was interrupted by a huge waterfall, dropping almost 4,000 feet from the mountain plateau above. Deciding that the island would provide good winter quarters, the trappers started clearing a portion of the land and erecting buildings.

Almost immediately, trouble broke out. Many Forest and Mountain Trolls attacked the explorers, with over half the expeditionary force being annihilated before they were able to retreat to the relative safety of the river. Sailing northward, they were surprised to find that they were being followed by Trolls who appeared to live in the water. Much to their relief, the River Trolls only escorted them for several miles.

The current emperor of Mamaryl, Kamrak VII, had been searching for a site near the center of the empire to

further with any matters relating to Jovian Falls.

Faced with the necessity of keeping the Jovian River open for travel year round (for, despite rumors to the contrary from the Emperor, there were still many Trolls in the area), the Duke utilized an annoying and dangerous element (the Trolls) to good advantage. Many River Trolls lived along the Jovian, keeping sections free of debris and holding up commerce (boats) with heavy chains until a passage fee was paid. Duke Borin sought out Ia Uprooter, the nominal Chief of the Jovian River Trolls, and offered him three times the total estimated revenue the Trolls would get from stopping ships for a year if he would organize the Trolls, remove all the chains (but keep them for defense purposes), and keep the river free of obstructions, debris, and ice.

Ia, not as dumb as he looked, spent some time bargaining with the Duke, received a sum 4½ times the normal amount and agreed to serve as peacemaker with the other types of Trolls in Mamaryl. The River Trolls, able to grasp the notion that they would get three times more money for less work, agreed to the plan. The traders and ship owners grumbled about the "Troll Taxes" levied on them by Duke Borin, but rapidly came to appreciate the value of faster travel time between stops and a diminished threat of losing a ship to new, uncharted obstructions in the river.

The situation has been peaceful for seventeen years. The Emperor has made no comment on the addition of several hundred Trolls to the Imperial work force. Ia Uprooter, in a spirit of comraderie, sent 12 Trolls to maintain the waterway around and upriver from the city of Jovian Falls. The Trolls also collected tolls for land traffic crossing the bridges into the city.

A side benefit of this association was that the Trolls of the Dread Forest to the north of Jovian Falls began to bring rare roots, herbs, plants, and flowers to the open air markets outside the city to trade for implements and trinkets. At first, they were cheated and given inferior goods. The Trolls protested to Ia, who in turn brought the matter to the Duke. Much to his credit, Duke Borin set up a board of trade to handle commerce with the Forest Trolls. As a result, the Trolls brought more goods to market and Jovian Falls was able to export some of the surplus. All seemed pleased with the situation, until a few months ago, when Mountain Trolls attacked overland convoys and a few ships anchored for the night.

develop as a commercial outpost to trade with the southern kingdoms. As this island seemed to provide a highly defensible position, the trappers were all rewarded with titles and a considerable amount of gold, and then ordered to guide a military expedition back to the island. They never returned.

Over the next seventy years, Kamrak and his son, Jambur, spent vast quantities of men and materials in eliminating the Troll menace from the island and surrounding areas. Roads were built to the coastal caravan routes and southward over the Black Wyvern Mountains. The island was ringed by a 30' high wall of imported stone and declared safe for habitation. Jambur immediately ordered merchants, chosen by lottery, to the new trading center. Reluctant to relocate to a distant island, these merchants soon made huge fortunes as the city of Jovian Falls did indeed become an important trading center.

Borin, Duke of Gammal and ruler of Jovian Falls for the past 20 years, has the heavy responsibility of maintaining the line of commerce to all parts of the kingdom. Shortly after being invested with his position, Duke Borin realized that he could not comply with the wishes of Emperor Caylos V unless more money, men, and arms were made available to him. Unfortunately, it soon became obvious that the Emperor, now living in the recently completed palace on Spider Isle (in the center of the giant Spiderweb Reef), did not wish to concern himself

1. THE WISHING WELL

This is a small natural well located to the southwest of the Palace. According to legend, anyone making a wish and dropping in some gold coins will have their wish granted. The first to discover this amazing property was said to be Alaric the Bold, one of the original explorers who discovered the island. It is said that his brother was severely wounded in the fight with the Trolls and in his (Alaric's) grief, he made a wish upon the well for a speedy recovery. The story has it that his brother soon experienced a miraculous recovery from his near-fatal wounds.

In truth, an enterprising merchant suspected that the presence of a wishing well should generate a nice income, made a big production of having been granted a wish, and invented the tale about Alaric! Over the years, he and his family have realized a steady income from this enterprise and have maintained the rumors of the well's supposed powers. Needless to say, there is nothing magical about the well, and any miracle resulting from wishing is a coincidence, nothing more. (If the party should cast a Detect Magic spell upon the well, it will register as magical. This is merely an aura to support the merchant's story, cast many years ago by a travelling wizard who owed the merchant a favor.)

2. THE TROLL APOTHECARY

Run by Umbarr Thickskin, a Forest Troll, the apothecary is one of the best sources of spell components in the city. The shop is located in Troll Town near the east gate of the city. Due to the neighborhood's high crime rate, it is not unusual to see magic users, escorted by many bodyguards, coming and going from his shop. Umbarr is scrupulously honest and deeply regrets anyone trying to cheat him, for his prices are very reasonable.

While not very bright, Umbarr is undeniably apt at locating many rare and valuable components and, as a result, has a good trade. (Umbarr knows most of the Forest Trolls in the area, and trades with them for most of his more common components, for they would rather deal with him than with the humans.)

3. THE RUNE STONE

The Rune Stone is a large outcrop of rock near the north wall of the city. This rock (10' tall by 3' wide by 12' long) is of an unknown type and of extreme hardness. To date, the Stone has resisted every attempt to crack or chip it without taking so much as a scratch. It is covered with unreadable runes and seems to be impervious to both physical and magical attacks of any kind. Needless to say, the Rune Stone is the source of a considerable number of rumors among both the humans and Trolls of the region. Predominant among the rumors is the following: Before the next major confrontation between good and evil, a hero will come to the lands from the west. He will decipher the Runes, shatter the stone, and lead the humans (or Trolls, depending on who is doing the talking) to victory over all who dare oppose them.

4. THE TROLL MUSEUM

Located just south of the Snake Gardens, the Troll Museum is a well-known attraction. It is a large wooden building with a breathtaking view of the gardens (especially the snakes) and the small donation required to enter (2 sp) is used to maintain the building and purchase curios for the Museum.

The chief curator is the Sage Arilan the Not-so-Tall, a recognized authority on things Trollish. He has spent his entire life studying Trolls and their habits and has a 90% chance of answering any question put to him concerning Trolls of this region.

DM NOTE: He does not yet know any details about the artifacts, but after they are discovered (if indeed they are), he will unearth some startling information regarding them. See the section entitled "The Flow of the Adventure" for more details on this information.

The curios found in the Museum include the following:

1. Human and other bone carvings (scrimshaws). One set, carved from the vertebrae of a giant, depicts a small caravan of humans and various pack beasts. Another presents an accurate representation of a Forest Troll village and its inhabitants at their daily tasks; it is carved from dragon bones.

2. A variety of wicker baskets, large and small, used by the River Trolls.

3. A display of many exotic and rare herbs traded by the Forest Trolls. This includes an extremely rare flower found in the Frozen Wastes called the Pityu, used in the manufacture of magical ink for the inscribing of spells of a cold-based nature.

4. Wooden, stone, and bone-tipped weapons built by Trolls, and a rare, ancient black-bladed sword manufactured by the Dark Trolls.

5. A clay plaque retrieved from the burial vault of a powerful Frozen Waste Troll Chief in the shape of a shield with designs that Arilan deciphered as a form of calendar depicting a 200 year cycle.
DM ONLY: This is in fact the Bronze Mask covered with dried and baked clay. No one knows its true nature. It does not register magically during the day. The baked-on clay will chip away readily to reveal the Bronze Mask beneath its outer shell.

6. A large collection of wooden, stone, clay, and metal ornamental masks used by the Trolls in their many ceremonies.

7. A large variety of cooking utensils of Troll origin, including a large stone bowl, measuring 1' across, thought to be used in the preparation of healing potions and salves. Inside the bowl are several smooth, round stones, of a size to fit in the palm of the hand (a Troll hand). It is suspected that they were used to grind dried herbs and roots in the bowl.
DM ONLY: One of the round stones is the Bronze Orb. It has been covered with clay and painted over with black paint; thus its true nature has gone unnoticed. (It is the only stone that does not really feel like rock, but this should not be told to the players unless they specifically state that they are examining all of the stones.) The Orb will not register as magical during the daylight hours.

DM ONLY: There will undoubtedly be parties that cannot, for whatever reason, locate the Mask and Orb. To allow you to counter the party's feelings of frustration and lack of direction, the following item has been provided. You may insert it into the adventure at an appropriate spot (i.e., in a treasure hoard, in one of the Troll Shaman burial sites, or hidden in a cavern); this will allow the party to "discover" a vital clue. Once "discovered," read the following to the party:

You have found what appears to be a polished thigh bone. About two inches below the bony knob on one end, a dark line circles the face of the shaft.

If the party pulls on the end of the bone, the knob will slip off, revealing a tightly-rolled skin secreted within the hollowed-out bone. When removed, the skin proves to be covered with strange writing (Trollish). The message can be read by any party member who can read Trollish, or by the Sage Arilan. It reads:

To My Dear Lilybane, first Speaker
and Guardian of the Sacred Relics,

I fear the battle to preserve our holy island will prove to be futile. There are too many bearded warriors with swords that burn and sticks that spit forth death. Our numbers are desperately low and I fear the enemy will soon break through our defenses. You can trust that we will never surrender, but I write concerning another matter.

The relics must not fall into the possession of the enemy, for they are the last symbols of our faith. Since I fear the end is near, I counsel you to secretly hide them among other ordinary items of no real value. Perhaps this will allow them to be overlooked so that we may recover them at a later date.

It is my sincerest wish that we meet next to celebrate our victory, but I feel the odds are not in our favor. Until then, I remain,

Your obedient servant,
Oakenthew, Chief Skullsplitter

5. THE TROLL TOTEMS

There are seven totems in the vicinity of the town, just outside the walls. They are great wooden carvings inlaid with bone. Each is in the form of some fierce, grimacing, humanoid creature. The totems are Mountain Troll grave posts and they mark the resting places of long-forgotten Troll Shamans. If the party digs beneath a totem, they will discover the bones of the Shaman, his tribal implements, and his personal treasure trove (consisting of copper jewelry and chains, ancient daggers, etc., 1-100 sp, and 1-10 gp).

DM ONLY: When a Troll Shaman is buried, his successor casts a curse that will affect anyone who disturbs the buried Shaman or any of his implements. Suggested curse ideas:

1. Bad Luck (-1 to hits and -1 to all saving throws), or

2. Monsters will become enraged at the sight of the cursed party member (they are +2 to hit and +3 to damage).

6. THE SHADY TREE INN

When the island was still being cleared for the construction of Jovian Falls, an immense tree of indeterminate species was discovered. Due to its huge size (roughly oval in shape and a little more than 80' in diameter), it was decided that the tree should be left standing as a "natural wonder." One of the first immigrants to the new city, an innkeeper, conceived a spectacular use for the tree when he found that though it was hollow at the core, it possessed a strong outer shell.

Asking for (and obtaining) permission, Imra Rosswald turned the tree into the city's first inn. There was room inside for three upper floors of sleeping rooms and a fourth smaller area used by the proprieter and his family. The ground floor of the inn consists of a dining room, bar, and the "common" sleeping room. The kitchen and bathing rooms are located in two outbuildings near the stable.

Since this is now a tourist attraction, the price of a room and board (even in the common room) is very expensive. The common room costs 1 gp per night, while private rooms are 5 gp per night. (The party is staying at this inn.) Should the party decide to try their luck searching for rumors, they will be well rewarded. Each character must roll a d20 under his appeal to determine whether the locals chose to impart their gossip to him. If the roll is successful, then a roll of d4 will determine the number of rumors heard. Roll a d20 on the chart below to discover which rumors were heard. It is entirely possible that a character will hear four rumors—all of them the same!

RUMORS

1. The Snake Garden is the dwelling place of the demon goddess of the Trolls. (false)

2. The Rune Rock, an outcrop near the north wall is impervious to all attempts to damage it. Only the touch of a great hero from the West will shatter the rock. (true)

3. Somewhere on the island is a secret entrance that leads to a tunnel complex beneath the island where the Dark Trolls once lived. (false)

4. There is an old abandoned Dark Troll cavern system somewhere in the uninhabited area near the town. (true)

5. The Wishing Well is the abode of a neutral demi-god. (false)

6. Strange Trolls have been seen at times in the vicinity of the Snake Gardens. (true)

7. Somewhere outside the town, within a week's journey, there is a long, lost (hidden) temple to the Troll god. (true)

8. Somewhere behind the great waterfall there is a secret entrance to the lair of an ancient Red Dragon. (false—it is a young Blue Dragon!)

9. Trolls fear the Haunted Forest near the northwest corner of the city, for a malign spirit dwells there. (true)

10. The Duke intends to use the 250,00 gp to raise an army and have himself crowned Emperor of Mamaryl. (false)

11. Trolls fear the touch of metal that has been rinsed in holy water. (false)

12. A number of people have disappeared near the vicinity of the Snake Gardens. (true) If questioned closely, it will be revealed that all who disappeared visited the gardens at night.

13. The Troll threat to the city is a scheme of the Duke's (working in collusion with the Trolls) to coerce additional tax monies from the citizens. (false)

14. A great Scythe, made of pure platinum, lies buried at the bottom of the Snake Garden. Called Troll-Bane, it was hidden there long ago by the Trolls to be guarded by the many snakes that live in the garden. (false)

15. The River Trolls have a vast labyrinth excavated beneath the riverbed where they plan for the overthrow of the Jovian settlers. (false)

16. Hidralla, the human sorceress who lives at the Shady Tree Inn, is the mistress of the local Mountain Troll Chieftain. (true—but she is visiting her lover for 2-12 days and will be most uncooperative when she returns)

17. The Duke's cousin and the River Troll Chieftain were waylaid on their journey, sacrificed, and eaten during a vile rite by Mountain Trolls. (false)

18. The delegation sent out by the Duke (his cousin and the River Troll Chieftain) are the leaders of the Troll uprising. (false)

19. The Duke has hired (conscripted) a group of adventurers passing through town to find the missing delegaton and either locate enough treasure to pay off the Troll demand or locate some long-lost artifacts that the Trolls want. (true)

20. The Duke has some Troll blood and is the real head of the Troll conspiracy. (false)

THE HAUNTED FOREST

The forested section in the southeast corner of the city is said to be haunted by the ghost of an evil priest of the Drow Elves who died on the island several hundred years ago. It is rumored the ghost will attack any who enter the forest alone at night. Over the years, many bodies of both races have been found, adding considerable credence to the

story. In fact, this is the spirit of one of the first explorers who died as a result of a Curse from the Troll Shaman fighting his group. The ghost will only attack Trolls who wander into the forest. Unfortunately, the few times he has appeared to humans, trying to beg for aid in being released from his curse, they died of fright at the sight of him.

Two hundred years ago, the forest was completely leveled in an effort to remove the hiding place of the ghost. It worked. The ghost moved into the royal palace. After six months, when all the clerics proved powerless to dislodge the spirit, the ruling Count had the trees replanted. The ghost returned to the forest and no further attempts have been made to dislodge him.

THE TEMPLES

Should the party members attempt to enlist the services of one of the temples in town, they will discover that while the clerics would be happy to be of assistance, they are far too busy on projects for the Duke to be of any help. (This means no Commune spells will be cast for them.)

THE SNAKE GARDENS

The fabled Snake Gardens, located by the south wall, were created from a great deep crevice. The sides of the crevice narrow as they descend in a series of shelflike protrusions. A great number of plants and shrubs grow on the shelves, thus obstructing the view to the bottom. No one is certain just how deep the crevice is.

A glance down will reveal that the entire garden complex is filled with snakes of all sizes, coloration and description. When the city was first built, there was talk of clearing out the snakes, but some of the merchants maintained that the spot was a natural wonder—as was the tree—and should be maintained, not destroyed. After many heated battles, it was decided that the gardens would be maintained. To that end, several Druids were hired to tend the Gardens and feed the snakes daily (and in great quantities) so that they would present no threat to the populace.

Though the gardens have always been a source of pride and wonder to the citizens of Jovian Falls, an underlying current of fear can be felt whenever they are discussed. It is widely believed that the Gardens are dangerous at night, since a few people who often ventured near them after sunset have disappeared. As a result, the area around the gardens is usually quite deserted during the dark hours.

On either side of the gardens are four large circular patterns, each measuring about five feet across. The patterns appear to be painted, but a closer examination will reveal that the designs are inlays of colored rock. All eight of the designs are different, but if examined closely, it will be obvious that they all appear to have a circular design, turning in a clockwise direction.

These patterns are a teleport system to the Troll Caverns, where the Troll Armies are massing. By day, they do not radiate magic and are non-functional, but at night they can be activated by simply walking the pattern in the direction that it turns. After turning in a complete circle (each pattern can only be walked by one person at a time, and it takes one melee round to do it), the person will be teleported to the matching pattern in the Troll Caverns.

Pattern 1 teleports to Level I, Room I
Pattern 2 teleports to Level I, Room A
Pattern 3 teleports to Level I, Room G
Pattern 4 teleports to Level II, Room E
Pattern 5 teleports to Level II, Room B
Pattern 6 teleports to Level III, Room H
Pattern 7 teleports to Level III, Room A
Pattern 8 teleports to Level III, Room D

ADVENTURE PART TWO
THE TROLL CAVERNS

The following section deals with the Troll Command Center, located in a natural limestone cavern about 15 miles from Jovian Falls. The party of adventurers will be able to find these caverns by either following the Troll delegation returning with the Duke's answer, or via the teleport patterns located at the Snake Gardens.

Should the party arrive by means of the teleport patterns, it will be necessary to determine where in the complex they will arrive. To do this, match the number of the teleport used in the Snake Gardens to the number of the teleport in the appropriate chamber in the caverns. Teleports 1, 2, and 3 are located on level I in rooms I, E, and G respectively; 4 and 5 are on level II in rooms E and B; 6, 7, and 8 are on level III in rooms H, A, and D. The monsters inhabiting these rooms have seen other creatures teleport in on occasion and should be considered ready to meet the adventurers when they arrive. Also, please note that the patterns in the caverns serves as receptors during the night hours, and senders (teleport back to Snake Gardens—see pattern list above) during the daylight hours.

The upper level of the caverns contains the Troll Command Center and houses the leaders of the Troll army camped outside. There are two teleport patterns located in the command room; the one marked A (featuring a clockwise pattern) will teleport the user back to the Snake Gardens—in the evenings only—and the one marked B with a counter-clockwise pattern) will teleport the user to the Troll Temple in the woods. The patterns in the Snake Gardens do not teleport players into the Command Center. Note also that the circular staircases, located in the entrance chamber on level I have Permanent Illusions of Stone cast upon them at the ceiling level. Unless a player physically attempts to touch the ceiling, or casts a spell to Detect Illusions, the false ceiling should not be discovered.

THE UPPER LEVEL
(COMMAND CENTER)

A   This is the barracks of six Dark Troll weaponsmiths [AC: 0, HTK: 39, 33, 32, 29, 27, 26 (6d8)]. The Trolls have a total of 248 gp.

B   In this room, the Troll Witchdoctor/Shaman Osgoth-Sogoth keeps his personal treasure. The room is seemingly unguarded and his treasure trove is in plain sight from the corridor. If the room is entered, the party will find themselves under attack by a Groaning Spirit [AC: 0, HTK: 50 (7d8)]. The Spirit is under the control of the Witchdoctor/Shaman and he is the only one who can enter the room without being attacked.

The treasure consists of 3,400 gp, 127 pp, 2 gems worth 150 gp each and a Robe of Camouflage (85% chance of blending into any background—fits mansize or smaller).

C This room is the lair of a female Ettin [AC: 3, HTK: 61 (10d8)] who is hopelessly in love with Osgoth-Sogoth. Her presence is tolerated only because she is an excellent bodyguard. She will fight fiercely (at +1) if he is present; if he is killed, she will go into a rage, gaining an extra attack each round. She has 18 gp.

D This is the barracks of a troop of Gnolls who fought and defeated other Gnolls for the priviledge of assisting their friends, the Trolls. The Gnoll leader, Swordbreaker [AC: 2, HTK: 38 (5d8)] has ring mail, a +3 large shield, a +2 battleaxe and a Potion of Extra-Healing. Godsmouth, a Witchdoctor [AC: 5, HTK: 39 (5d8)] has ring mail, a shield, a mace and dagger, a Ring of Wizardry (doubles 1st and 2nd level spells) and a scroll containing two 2nd level spells (DM's choice).

The twelve Gnolls [AC: 5, HTK: 36, 36, 37, 33, 30, 28, 32, 29, 28, 32, 29, 31 (4d8)] all wear ring mail, carry shields, and are armed with broadswords and halberds. Four Gnolls carry longbows instead of halberds.

E This is the quarters for the 20 Frozen Waste Trolls [AC: 4, HTK: 51, 50, 48, 46, 45, 41, 37, 37, 33, 32, 30, 30, 30, 29, 28, 28, 27, 26, 26, 25 (8d8)] that serve as the personal bodyguards of the Troll leaders found in the Command Center.

F These are secret doors leading to the Command Center. They are convex in shape and appear to be the "natural" end of the tunnels they are in. The mechanism to open them is very simple to operate, but if done incorrectly, will trigger a dead fall trap in the ceiling. The falling rocks will do 4d6 of damage to anyone in the last 15' of the corridor and will warn the Trolls in the Command Center. To open the doors, it is necessary to apply a combined strength of 36 pts. to the left side of the door (up to three people may push at one time) and the door will pivot open. If the party tries to push on the right hand side of the door, the trap will be sprung.

G These areas are the entrances for this level. In each cavern is a Common Troll Sargeant [AC: 5, HTK: 35, 37 (7d8)] guard. Attached to one wall is a heavy rope ladder that will be lowered to level I on request.

THE COMMAND CENTER

This rather large cavern is a combination shrine, meeting room, and living quarters for the leaders of the Trolls. On the west wall of the room, there is a small altar with a gold statue of the Snake God (worth 750 gp). In the center of the room is a large wooden table which supports a very crude map of the area and the city of Jovian Falls. The location of the Snake Temple is marked on the map with the notation "Arksnout" scrawled in Trollish. The east end of the room is partitioned larged areas that serve as sleeping quarters. There are three Mountain Troll guards stationed near each of the doors leading in to this room. The occupants of this room are: Osgoth-Sogoth, the Witchdoctor/Shaman leader of the Troll army, six 5th skill Troll Shamans, and two 5th skill Troll Withdoctors. Osgoth-Sogoth is a very large Two Headed Troll.

On the east wall, near the north wall, are two teleport patterns. One pattern has a complex clockwise design; walking it will transport the person randomly to one of the patterns around the Snake Gardens in Jovian Falls (roll a d8 to determine the specific pattern). The other pattern has a counter-clockwise design; it will teleport those that walk it to the Troll Temple, the home of the Two Headed Troll Patriarch Arksnout.

6 Mountain Troll Guards [AC: 3, HTK: 48, 45, 36, 35, 29, 41 (8d8+6)]

1 Desert Troll Shaman [AC: 4, HTK: 60 (10d8)].
   Skill: 5. Spells Known (3/3/1): Cure/Cause Light Wounds, Protection from Good, Resist Fire, Augury, Chant, Snake Charm, Dispell Magic.

3 Hill Troll Shamans [AC: 5, HTK: 67, 56, 49 (11d8)]
   Skill: 5. Spells known (3/3/1): Same as Desert Troll Shaman above.

2 Dark Troll Witchdoctors [AC: 1, HTK: 50, 42 (9d8)].
   Skill: 4. Spells Known (3/2): Affect Normal Fires, Shield, Ventriloquism, Invisibility, Levitate.

Osgoth-Sogoth [AC: 4, HTK: 63 (12d8)]
  Right Head (Skill: 4), Shaman Spells Known (3/2): Cure/Cause Light Wounds, Detect Magic, Resist Fire, Chant, Snake Charm.
  Left Head (Skill: 4), Witchdoctor Spells Known (3/2): Identify, Shield, Ventriloquism, Invisibility, Detect Invisibility.

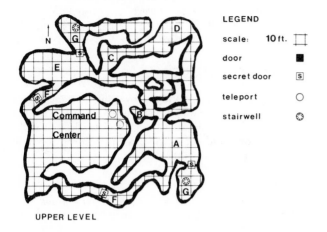

LEGEND

scale:	10 ft.
door	■
secret door	S
teleport	○
stairwell	✳

UPPER LEVEL

CAVERN LEVEL I

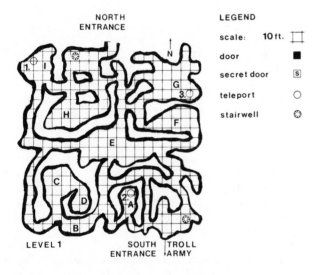

LEGEND

scale:	10 ft.
door	■
secret door	S
teleport	○
stairwell	✳

NORTH ENTRANCE

If the group has followed the returning Troll Delegation, they will enter the complex via the northern entrance cavern. This room is guarded by three Common Trolls [AC: 5, HTK: 30, 28, 25 (4d8)].

SOUTH ENTRANCE

In the small northern cavern of this area, four Gnolls [AC: 5, HTK: 28, 32, 30, 27 (4d8)] guard the entrance. For every 5 minutes the party watches the stairwell, there is a 15% chance of a Troll entering from the valley to the south. If a Troll does enter, it is likely that he will approach the stairwell, shout for the ladder, and climb to the level above. The ladder will then be drawn up again. Otherwise, the Troll is just checking on the guards and will return to the valley.

If the party proceeds to the valley south of the caverns, they will discover the assembled Troll army. It is huge; the army is spread over such a large area, the party should not want to try sneaking around in the valley. However, in case the party tries to attack, here is a breakdown of the army camped in the valley:

	Normal	Leaders	Shamans	Witchdoctors
Common	385	20	4	2
Dark	79	12	5	5
Desert	7	1	1	2
Frozen Waste	156	25	7	1
Hill	47	4	1	3
Mountain	190	14	10	12
Giant	8	2	0	1
Two Headed	11	2	2	1
Trorcs	51	5	1	0

An additional number of Trolls equivalent to approximately 20% of the above force will be on patrol, gathering food and blocking the rivers and all roads. The Trolls will not pay much attention to small independent parties, but will definitely attack any ship or caravan that they spot. These Trolls travel in groups of 2d10; composition of the groups is mixed as all the above Troll types are united in the effort to recover the holy ground. The Forest and River Trolls, convinced that the citizens of Jovian Falls have not stolen the Bronze Mask and Orb, have decided to remain neutral in the impending battle.

DM NOTE: In the two entrance caverns on this level, a large, wooden staircase can be seen. It appears to be firmly attached to the ceiling and descends into the darkness of the levels below. The natural rock ceiling at the top of this staircase is a Permanent Illusion; the Trolls climb through it into the command level above. Unless a Detect Illusion spell is cast or the ceiling is physically checked, the illusionary nature of the ceiling should not be discovered. Note that the steps on the staircase start at this level and proceed downward, but the supports for the stairwell run to the ceiling. The cavern is 25' tall, but the walls are rough and easily climbable by thieves. The Trolls use a heavy rope ladder, attached to the wall in the cavern above. A Troll guard is stationed in this cavern; he will drop the rope ladder when anyone shouts "Let me up!" or its equivalent in Trollish. The lower levels contain various monsters which the Trolls have decided to leave alone. They serve as a deterrent to unwanted visitors.

A   This room is the lair of two Minotaurs [AC: 6, HTK: 33, 39 (6d8+3)]. They are friendly with the Trolls and serve as guards for the teleport pattern in this room. The teleport pattern in this room works in conjuction with teleport pattern 2 at the Snake Gardens.

B   This is the lair of three Carrion Crawlers [AC: 3/7, HTK: 21, 16, 25 (3d8+1)]. There are 85 sp and 2 small 10 gp gems mixed in with the bones of their victims.

C   This room is the home of a colony of Giant Centipedes. There are 22 of them [AC: 7, HTK: 6 each (1d8)] located all over the room on the floors, walls, and ceiling. They have no treasure.

D   This room is empty, except for a teleport pattern which works with pattern 1 at the Snake Gardens.

E   A Trapper [AC: 3, HTK: 54 (12d8)] resides near the center of this large cavern. The Trolls all know of its location and avoid walking over it.

F   This is the lair of a Giant Slug [AC: 3, HTK: 63 (12d8)]. There are pools of acid in depression in the floor. They have been partially neutralized by the limestone of the caverns. Anyone exploring a pool with their hand will take 1-4 points damage and have a 15% chance of finding 1-3 gp.

G   This room is empty, except for a teleport pattern which works with pattern 3 at the Snake Gardens.

H   There are four coffins made of stone in this room. In each coffin is a Spectre who will resent his rest being disturbed! Each Spectre has 200 gp in treasure; one has a Ring of Spell Storing with a Cure Serious Wounds spell still in it.
4 Spectres [AC: 2, HTK: 37, 32, 36, 32 (7d8+3)]

I   As the group approaches this cavern's entrance, they will become aware of a reddish glow coming from within. When they enter, they will discover that the glow comes from nine Fire Beetles [AC: 4, HTK: 9, 14, 11, 7, 5, 12, 9, 13, 11 (2d8+2)], in the northern portion of the caverns. There is also a large pile of fungus and rotted vegetation; it contains nothing of value.

CAVERN LEVEL II

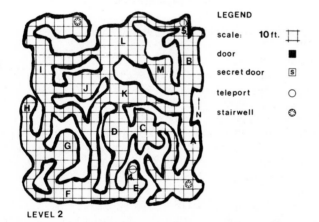

LEGEND

scale: 10 ft.

door

secret door

teleport

stairwell

LEVEL 2

A   There is a pit in the center of this room, 5'x5'x20' deep. The last 15' of the pit is filled with water. The surface of the pit is covered and appears to be a solid part of the floor. Anyone falling in the pit will take 2-12 points of damage and must also risk drowning. A character wearing metal armor will drown in 6-10 rounds. In addition, any character falling in will have a 15% chance of striking their head on a protruding rock during the fall, losing consciousness, and immediately drowning.

B   This is the lair of four Giant Tarantulas [AC: 3, HTK: 31, 29, 20, 22 (5d8+3)]. They have 1 attack for 3-12 points of damage plus poison. They have no treasure. The teleport pattern in this chamber works in conjunction with pattern 5 at the Snake Gardens.

C   This is the home of twelve Piercers [AC: 3, HTK: 2, 3, 5 (1d8); 5, 11, 14 (2d8); 15, 19 (3d8); 16, 21, 20, 27 (4d8)]. In the northwest corner of the room, near the ceiling, there hangs a leather pouch containing jewels worth 21,000 gp

D   This room is unoccupied.

E   Clinging to the ceiling above the entrance to this cavern is a Black Pudding [AC: 6, HTK: 54 (10d8)]. The ceiling is about 30' high and torch light will not reveal its presence. It will attempt to drop on the first party member to enter/exit the room.

F   This is the lair of three Cockatrices [AC: 6, HTK: 20, 21, 27 (5d8)]. They eat the seed casing of the foul-smelling luminous moss that grows in this cavern.

G   In this cavern are three Violet Fungi [AC: 6, HTK: 24, 25, 20 (5d8)].

H   At the entrance to this cavern is a covered pit, 10'x10'x40' deep. Trapped in the pit is a Gelatinous Cube [AC: 8, HTK: 25 (4d8)]. Beneath the Cube is a Dwarf's skeleton, 14 gp, a +2 hammer and a +1 shield.

I   There is a pit in the center of this room 10'x10'x20' deep. The last 15' of the pit is filled with water. The surface of the pit is covered and appears to be a solid part of the floor. Anyone falling in the pit will take 2-12 points of damage and must also risk drowning. A character wearing metal mail will drown in 6-10 rounds. In addition, any character falling in will have a 15% chance of striking their head on a protruding rock during the fall, losing consciousness, and immediately drowning.

J   This room contains a Lurker Above [AC: 6, HTK: 65 (10d8)]. If bribed, the Lurker will provide the party with complete details of this level and its inhabitants. He knows where the exits are and has never seen a Troll on this level.

K   This room is empty.

L   This room is empty.

M   This room contains an Ochre Jelly [AC: 8, HTK: 39 (6d9)]

CAVERN LEVEL III

The air on this level has an unpleasant, moldy, murky smell to it. There is a 2" deep layer of slimy water on the floor and the walls are all damp and slippery (reduce wall climbing ability by 25%). The average air temperature here is about 80 degrees and there is a +10% chance for each player to contract a disease (if such rules are being used).

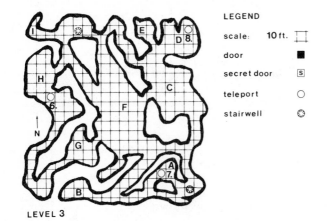

LEGEND

scale:	10 ft.
door	■
secret door	S
teleport	○
stairwell	✦

LEVEL 3

A This room contains two Ghasts [AC: 4, HTK: 20, 22 (4d8)]. They have no treasure. The pattern in this room will teleport players to pattern 7 at the Snake Gardens.

B This room contains a Shreiker [AC: 7, HTK: 20 (3d8)].

C This room contains a Shambling Mound [AC: 0, HTK: 52 (10d8)], and a large growth of orange-green luminescent mushrooms.

D This room is empty except for the teleport pattern that works in conjunction with pattern 8 at the Snake Gardens.

E This room is empty.

F This room is empty.

G This room is empty.

H This room contains a wandering Umber Hulk [AC: [AC: 2, HTK: 45 (8d8)]. It also contains a pattern that is linked to pattern 6 in the Snake Gardens.

I This room contains four Ghasts [AC: 4, HTK: 24, 20, 18, 16 (3d8)]. They have no treasure.

THE TROLL TEMPLE OF THE SNAKES

The temple is located in an abandoned Dark Troll mining complex. The site was abandoned for about 50 years prior to the arrival of the priests and, as a result, many of the abandoned tunnels are inhabited. The area around the mine entrance is heavily forested and may be easily overlooked if the party is not specifically searching for it. When passing by the area, rangers have a 9% chance of noticing the entrance, other classes only a 4% chance. Since all the priests use the patterns to enter and leave the complex, there are no obvious trails leading to the entrance.

If the party approaches the complex from the outside, ignoring the patterns and following the crude map found in the Control Center of the Troll Caverns, there is a good chance they will encounter one of the groups of forest monsters surrounding the site.

Approaching from the northwest, there is a 65% chance that the party will encounter a Goblin pack led by Jarith the Mocker. Jarith [AC: 3, HTK: 18 (3d8+3)], wears a +3 Ring of Protection and Bracers of AC: 3, and weilds a sword. His three subleaders are Assassins [AC: 6, HTK: 11, 12, 9 (3d6)], and the rest of the tribe (31 in number) are Fighter/Thieves, [AC: 6, HTK: 9 each (2d8)]. Their hoard consists of cured hides worth 250 gp, 312 cp, 56 sp, and 157 gp.

Approaching from the southwest, there is an 80% probability of an encounter with a group of Owlbears [AC: 5, HTK: 40, 38, 35, 33, 29 (4d8+2)]. They are vicious and always attack those intruding into their area. Their loot consists of six 25 gp gems and a Wand of Snare and Pit Detection (22 charges left).

Approaching from the southeast, there is a 50% chance of an encounter with a tribe of 25 Orcs of the Dark Weasel Tribe. The four leaders are Were-Weasels [AC: 4, HTK: 35, 32, 28, 23 (5d8+2)]. They wear leather armor, and attack once per round for 1-10 points of damage using heavy broadswords. The other 21 Orcs [AC: 6, HTK: 11 each (2d8+2)] also have high dexterity which they use to retreat when they are outmatched in any fight. They have accumulated six gold rings, four silver armbands, 165 gp, and two miscellaneous scrolls (DM's choice).

Approaching from the east, the party will probably (75% chance) meet 1-4 Wyverns [AC: 3, HTK: 55, 50, 45, 32 (7d8+7)]. Their lair is located at the edge of the forest, three miles due east of the Troll Temple. Having recently moved into the area, their lair contains nothing of value.

If the party approaches from the northeast, there is a 35% chance they will meet two Gorgons [AC: 2, HTK: 42, 39 (8d8)] passing through the area. One of the Gorgons has a +2 Dagger imbedded in its hide; otherwise, they have no treasure. Their lair is many miles distant.

LEVEL ONE

The main tunnel for Level 1 of the complex is 20' wide and 25' tall. Thirty feet inside the main entrance are two guard stations, each manned by a Common Troll [AC: 5, HTK: 29, 32 (4d8)]. The main entrance and the staircase in Cavern 8 are guarded by invisible glyphs which are activated by an astral, invisible, or ethereal creature attempting to gain entrance to the Temple. Each glyph will brilliantly outline any creature which activates it; this glow is only dispelled when the recipient leaves the Temple area.

1, 2, 3, 4 These caverns are all empty. Four mining shafts extend from each cavern in a prime example of the Dark Troll's mining techniques. Each shaft has a 30% chance of containing small monsters (i.e. Giant Rats, Large Spiders, baby Carrion Crawlers, or Giant Centipedes).

Just past the entrances to Caverns 1, 2, and 3, two teleport patterns will be noticed. Just beyond the teleport patterns are two more guard stations. Each station is manned by a Giant Troll [AC: 4, HTK: 52, 45 (8d8)].

The eastern pattern is formed into a complex clockwise design. It serves as the recieving station for the teleport pattern located in the Troll Caverns command center. The western pattern, a simple counter-clockwise design, will teleport anyone turning in a counter-clockwise direction to the receiving pattern in the same room in the Troll Caverns.

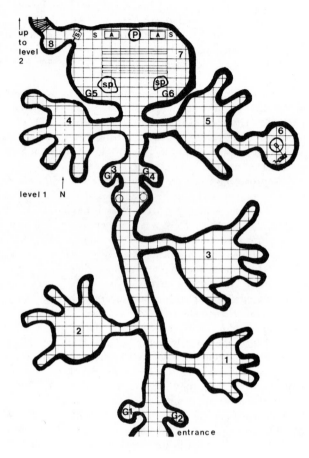

LEGEND

scale:	10 ft.	▢	stairway	⫿⫿
door	■		sacrificial pit	Ⓟ
secret door	Ⓢ		alter	Ⓐ
teleport	○		snake pit	ⓢⓟ
stairwell	✪		statue	s
			guardpost	G

5   On the ceiling of the tunnel running to Cavern 5, a solitary subterranean Lizard [AC: 4, HTK: 27 (5d8+2)] waits. It has three attacks, 1-4, 1-4, 1-10, and will spring upon the last party member as he passes beneath it. In Cavern 5 are two Boring Beetles [AC: 3, HTK: 25, 31 (5d8)] who will attack when the party enters.

6   If the party proceeds to Cavern 6, they will notice a deep shaft sunk into the earth. A winch and pully located in this cavern can be used to raise from and lower objects into the mine shaft. This pully system and rope are in excellent condition; it can support a ton of material.

7   This is a large worship chamber. Near the southern entrance are two small snake pits, each guarded by a skill one Dark Troll Shaman [AC: 4, HTK: 38, 36 (6d8)]. They each know the Protection From Good

spell. Large benches fill the center of the cavern. At the north end are two solid onyx altars, a 30' deep sacrificial pit, and two solid gold snake idols worth 300 gp each. In the northwest corner of the cavern is a secret door. Opening it will reveal a small room (Cavern 8).

8   This cavern is guarded by a skill 2 Common Troll Witchdoctor [AC: 5, HTK: 48 (8d8)]. The staircase climbing steeply upward has an invisible glyph guarding it (see above).

Descending the vertical shaft in Cavern 6, the party will discover that there are six horizontal mine shafts leading from it:

9   This cavern is a small guard post; its entrance is covered with a grey hide and is difficult to spot. If the Hill Troll guard [AC: 4, HTK: 40 (6d8+8)], spots intruders descending into the depths, he will wait until the platform passes and will then cut the rope (6d8 damage caused by the fall).

10   This cavern is empty.

11   A Giant Scorpion [AC: 3, HTK: 31 (5d5+5)] is here.

12   This cavern is very treacherous and extremely damp. The only occupant is a migrating Grey Ooze [AC: 2, HTK: 40 (5d8)].

13   This large cavern at the end of the shaft is completely deserted and is in a very dangerous condition. On a roll of 1-4 on a d8, part of the roof will cave in doing 3d10 points of damage, no saving throw allowed.

14   The captured party is here. They are firmly shackled to the walls and are guarded by an Efreet [AC: 2, HTK: 60 (10d8)].

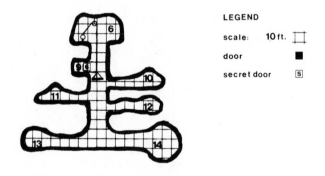

LEGEND

scale:	10 ft.	▢
door		■
secret door		Ⓢ

LEVEL TWO

The stairway leading up from Cavern 8 is quite steep and difficult to climb without having both hands free. Going up the creaky stairs without the benefit of a Silence spell will attract the attention of the guards in Room 16. Thieves have a normal chance of escaping detection.

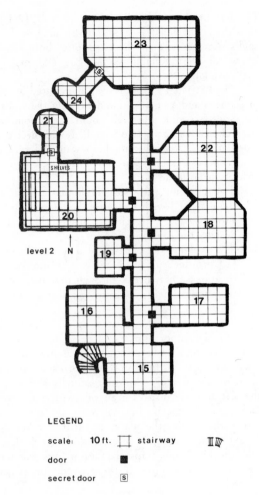

LEGEND

scale: **10** ft. ▢ stairway ⫘

door ◼

secret door Ⓢ

15 This room is empty. There are pegs on the west wall. Some hold normal cloaks and robes.

16 Clerical guard room. Seven Mountain Troll guards [AC: 3, HTK: 33, 31, 27, 25, 24, 26, 29 (6d8+6)] wearing padded fire-resistant armor (+2 save vs. fire), are watching the stairs. If noise comes from level one, all guards will be hiding around the corner. A normal guard station, there is nothing of value in this room.

17 This serves as a sleeping/meditation room for three Mountain Troll Deacons (skill 5 Shamans [AC: 3, HTK: 53, 47, 45 (13d8+6)]). Two are sleeping; the other is studying at a desk. In the room are 6 hammocks, a large table, 8 chairs, 10 chests, and 4 bags (containing 32 sets of soiled Troll clerical garb). Each Troll uses a very large mace (1d12+3 damage) and knows the following spells:

Cause Light Wounds, Detect Magic, Protection From Good, Resist Fire, Chant, Snake Charm, Cause Blindness

18 Oshtiosh, a skill 7 Dark Troll Shaman [AC: 2, HTK: 67 (12d8)], resides here. He wears +1 plate armor, wields a +3 mace, and carries a Wand of Magic Missiles with 12 charges left. In the room are several tables with chairs, a large bed, and five chamber pots (3 full). There is a bookcase with several clerical tomes, clerical lists, and ledgers (all written in Trollish). On the walls are three tapestries of good quality, but in need of

repair. The tapestry on the north wall covers a secret door. Ostiosh knows the following spells:

Protection From Good, Darkness, Cause Light Wounds, Augury, Resist Fire, Chant, Cause Disease, Poison.

19 Centered against the west wall is a 20'x20'x6' pool which is filled by water seeping from a crack in the stone wall. The overflow is channelled into another hole which disappears back into the solid rock. The water is clear and safe to drink.

20 This room contains many items of an evil nature. The secret door in the north wall is not easily seen (15% chance for Dwarves, 5% for others). The mechanism for opening the door is a small statue on a shelf in the northwest corner. If the statue is moved to the left, the door opens. If moved to the right, a beam shoots from the statue's eyes striking the mover. The effects of the beam are:

1. Complete memory loss for 2-7 days. The affected player will be absolutely unable to perform any but the most elementary functions (walk, eat, etc.).

2. All magical abilities of items carried by the player struck by the beam are neutralized for a period 1d4 times as long as the memory loss. The items will not register as magical during this period. Note that all the other magic items in the room have a 15% chance of also being affected (no saving throw allowed).

21 The 20' of corridor leading to Cavern 21 is permanently dark. The room is occupied by Desert Raven, a skill 7 Desert Troll Shaman [AC: 4, HTK: 88 (12d8)] and his mace, Skull Crusher. The weapon is intelligent (ego 13) and telepathic. The mace hates magic users and will direct Desert Raven to strike them in the head. If the magic user in the party cannot be reached by Skull Crusher, a Disintegration Ray 30' long will shoot forth each round at a random magic user. If the beam strikes someone in front of the magic user, so be it. Desert Raven knows all the available Shaman spells, but seldom uses them, preferring to fight using the mace.

The Mace is evil in disposition and will corrupt anyone who uses it, regardless of previous acts of alignment (i.e. even nasty creatures become nastier). While the actual identity of the personality inhabiting the Mace is not known, rumor has it that the soul of a fallen patriarch abides within.

The room contains several very expensive Trollish chairs, a couch, a very large four-poster bed, several wall sconces and two small tables. Hidden in the bed are two small coffers, each containing the skull of a dead arch-mage. The eye sockets are gen-encrusted and the teeth are golden plated. While both skulls give off a magical aura, this is only due to the preliminary incantations; nothing will happen if the party tries to use them. Desert Raven's treasure is concealed in the four bed posts. The top of each post unscrews (thus releasing a Spectre [AC: 2, HTK: 37, 34, 30, 29 (7d8+2)] from within), revealing the incredible amount of gems Desert Raven has accumulated. There are approximately 10,000 gp worth of gems hidden this way. The skulls are worth 800 gp apiece.

22 This room serves as the living quarters for the six female acolytes that serve Arksnout, the Troll Patriarch. They are level 3 Hill Troll Shamans [AC: 4, HTK: 36, 34, 33, 30, 28, 28 (9d8)] who know the following spells (3/1):

Protection From Good, Create Water, Sanctuary, and Chant or Resist Fire.

The room contains 6 beds and dressers as well as several wooden closets which cover the secret door. The closet can only be moved by those with a strength of 18 or better. The acolytes have 25 gp secreted in one of the dressers.

J. CLOUSE '82

23 The chief instigator of the Troll invasion of Jovian Falls is the Two-Headed Troll Shaman/Shaman Patriarch Arksnout [AC: 2, HTK: 88 (14d8)]. Arksnout, a light sleeper, is resting at the moment, but any loud noise in the corridor or in Room 22 will awaken him. He is armed with an Adder Staff of the Serpent, a +3 mace and an amulet which allows him to contact the Snake Demon (see Cavern 24, the treasury). He is totally immune to snakes and has a Spirit Naga [AC: 4, HTK: 49 (9d8)] as a bodyguard. The Naga is awake and alert, but can be surprised.

Arksnout possesses the following attributes: Strength: 19(00), Dexterity: 12, Stamina: 12. His left head has Intellect: 16, Insight: 17, and Appeal: 14, while his right head is Int.:15, Ins.:16, and App.: 8.

The left head is a skill 7 Shaman with 3/3/2/1 spells, and the right head is a skill 6 Shaman with 3/3/2 spells. At the time of the encounter, both heads will know all the available spells. The DM may select spells available.

The Patriarch's room is well illuminated by torches in sconces and a crystal chandelier. On the walls hang six tapestries and, scattered about the room, are six large chairs. There are two large beds and three gigantic wooden closets on the northern wall. A large display case contains several war momentos and two scrolls written in Trollish:

Scroll 1 explains the basic Troll plan for attacking the city of Jovian Falls (use the teleports from the Troll Caverns to teleport inside the walls and destroy the town).

Scroll 2 explains the back-up plan of attack: sacrifice Ia Uprooter's party to their Snake Goddess hoping to appease her. Break through the city walls with the goddess' help to regain their holy ground).

The door in the southwest wall leads to the treasury. The door appears to be securely bolted and locked by at least two different mechanisms of obvious sensitivity and difficulty (-30% to each attempt to open or deactivate). The door actually slides open to the left and will do so for anyone with a 19 strength. Picking and deactivating will only set off an alarm inside the vault (the alarm is silent, awakening the demon within. There is only a 15% chance of detecting that the locks and traps are false if someone actually attempts to determine if the are odd or unusual in nature.

24 This is obviously a treasure storeroom. When the players first enter the vault, they will notice 25 large statues of a snake demon. One of them is a real demon and will not move or attack until it is able to successfully determine the nature, intentions, and abilities of the creatures entering the cavern. When first looked upon, he will simply appear to be one more statue, due to the silvery color of his scales. His 5' long arms will mimic the exact posture of the other statues in the room. If the party appears weak or severely hurt, he will attack the first creature that approaches. If the party appears to be too strong to attack, he will gate out after he has gotten as much information as possible. He will then wait until a proper moment presents itself, gate back into the cavern complex, and attack the intruders singly as each opportunity is presented. Brysil is patient and cunning; play him that way.

The large snake demon Brysil [AC: -3, HTK: 90 (12d8)] has 40% magic resistance. He is very intelligent and has four attacks: two claw attacks (2-8 points damage each), one bite (1-12 damage, save vs. poison at -3), and a tail (1-8 initial damage—3-18 per round of constriction). In addition, he possesses all normal demon abilities.

Scattered around the treasure are the following: 20,539 cp, 34,006 sp, 20,563 gp, 345 ep, 10 clerical scrolls containing two spells each (levels 1-5), two Candles of Invocation, six Potions of Fire Immunity (useable by Trolls only, others save vs. poison). In a very ornate chest (locked and trapped) are the four gold and gem-encrusted skulls of previous Troll patriarchs worth 800 gp each. Anyone of neutral or good alignment who handles a skull will immediately take 2d10 points of damage. The trap on the chest will, if sprung, fill the treasury and Cavern 23 with poison gas (all must save vs. poison at -3; those that save, take 3d8 damage from caustic fumes).

In a silver scroll tube is an elegant document which details the powers innate in the Bronze Mask and Orb. It is also very explicit in its warning not to let anything happen to them while the Snake Goddess Lirabyth is on the material plane; they become brittle in her presence. Accidental destruction of the artifacts will banish her from this plane forever. See the section on Troll Gods and Rituals in the text for details on Lirabyth.

ORCISH CULTURE

By Robert L. Asprin

Orcs!!

The very word summons vivid images to the mind of any Tolkien fan. Hordes of squat dark figures with glowing eyes squabbling, brawling, bickering . . . these mothers are BAD!! In fact, they're so bad, one wonders how it is possible to put such a force into the field, much less control it effectively in battle. I mean, if the other side can just lean back for a couple hours or a day at most, the Orc army will probably wipe *itself* out. Right?

Don't bet your life on it!

As with any soldier, to understand the Orc warrior, one must first understand the culture that spawned him. ["Orc Culture?" the editor screams, "There ain't no such animal! What're you trying to pull, Asprin?"] A moment out for semantics: Most hairy chested men and women who play FRP games think of Culture as Music, Art, Literature, and sissy stuff like that. The same applies to hairy eared FRP supplement editors. When *I* refer to culture, I am not speaking of the cultur*al* pursuits of a group, but rather its very structure. Going a little too fast for you Bunky? Let me try again a little slower for the media buffs.

Roaming individuals, acting independently of each other, constitute an Anarchy . . . that is, no leader or government. When individuals band together for the common good and adopt a set of laws, traditions, or customs to guide their behavior and interaction, that group becomes a tribe, society, or civilization. Climate, economic conditions, population pressures, etc. combine to dictate what manner of customs, laws, and government are effective for the group, and that overall living structure is referred to as the group's culture.

What I am proposing is that while we know *how* an Orc acts, we won't know *why* he acts that way until we understand the society/culture that spawned him.

Okay? Onward!

Orcs are primarily carnivorous (meat eaters) unlike humans who are omnivorous (will eat anything: plant, animal, and otherwise). The mere thought of having to eat a root or fungus is enough to send a full-grown male Orc into a frenzied search for any meat to eat. Only when faced with starvation, will the Orc sense of dignity allow them to partake of (shudder!) roots, nuts berries, or fruits.

Bad as these dietary restrictions are, consider the plight of Orcs stranded in remote areas (i.e. mountain plateaus or desert islands). Unable to find fresh meat after they had exterminated the local populations (Orcs are not big on conservation or planning for the future), they were forced to eat large quantities of materials that had

heretofore comprised only a small portion of the Orc diet. In the face of the relentless onslaught of vegetation, the Orc physiological system rebels. A dormant gland is activated by large amounts of digested chlorophyll and the substance it secretes creates within the Orc a complete inability to digest anything but meat. Biologically speaking, this puts them at a distinct disadvantage.

Orcs originally banded together into tribes because, as individuals, they were too often easy prey for the food animals they hunted. As a consequence, Orcs spent most of their time killing each other for food. Eventually, Orcs bowed to the pressures brought by their Shamans, formed

alliances, and grouped together in the common cause of getting the next meal on the table.

Unfortunately this was not as good an idea as it originally seemed. The Orcs as a society became too successful and mathematics caught up with them. Mathematics? Right. Figure it out yourself. While the Orcs were killing each other, their population growth was stunted. Once they made peace, there were the same number of little Orcs being born. More Orcs mean higher food requirements, but hunting as groups they were able to increase the take for the pot. Terrific! Except for mathematics (again). Again, figure it out. With more food animals being killed, there were fewer births to replenish the food population. In short, as the population of Orcs grew, their food sources shrank. The end result was inevitable . . . a lot of Orcs, with not enough food to go around.

There was an obvious solution to this problem, and the Orcs took it. It's called cannibalism. Having your relatives for dinner took on a whole different meaning in Orc society. Only one fact saved the Orcs from following this solution right into extinction . . . Orc meat tastes awful. Imagine the worst meat you can think of left in the sun for several weeks while the flies do their thing with it, then dip it in something unpleasant and try to gag it down and you'll have a rough idea of the appetizing nature of Orc meat.

Now then, if you were an Orc faced with an endless diet of Orc meat, you too would be inspired to seek about for the other obvious solution: If there's no food left in your territory, then expand your territory! What's that? There's someone else living in the territory next door? Even better! They've *got* to taste better than Orc!

Okay, that gives you an overview of the situation. How does that trickle down (an Orcish expression) to the individual?

In a society involving cannibalism, the weak are the first to go. This gives the individual the greatest possible incentive to establish and maintain a "strong" front. In Orcdom, one plays macho games for keeps. It should be remembered, however, that another facet of survival requires that one *not* try to push around a rival who really *is* stronger.

The strongest/meanest individuals are designated as the front line troops for the society's expansion program. These are much sought after positions, as a victory brings not only glory, but a decent meal as well. Discipline in an Orcish army is terrible, not just because of the macho thing, but also there is no drive for maximum effectiveness. Orcs don't mind extra casualties among their own kind. If they win, there'll be fewer to share the food with. If they lose, Orc meat isn't really all *that* bad, and besides, it's easier to dine on a fallen comrade than to *personally* kill off one that's still healthy and fighting.

This brings us to the one area of military effectiveness practiced by the Orcs. Orcs are *not* big on organized fighting. They're big on winning. They will win with the least fighting (read personal risk to the individual) possible. This pragmatic approach to combat allows them to strike without warning, preferably from behind or while their target is asleep, without experiencing the slightest bit of guilt over violating a code of honor. Men of honor would do well to carefully study and consider this philosophy. It may be why Orcs are flourishing and expanding their territories while men of honor are on the endangered species list!

It is important to note that however disorganized and undisciplined an Orc army may appear, they do not suffer from a shortage of morale. If the alternative to facing the enemy and risking a quick death is returning home and starving to death, the army is going to stand firm.

Friendships are rarely permanent in Orcish culture. There are alliances where two individuals neither attack nor run from each other, and mutual co-operation will bring benefit to both. Unfortunately, such alliances only last until a better deal happens along, or until one individual realizes the trust shown by the other is a golden opportunity to . . .

By now you should have the picture. Day to day life as an Orc is the pits (which as any Orc will tell you is the hard center of an Elf). Perhaps the only thing worse than being an Orc is seeing one across the top of your shield. Better kill him, Bunky, because he's not about to stop until one of you is dead.

ORCS

By Les Kay

INTRODUCTION

Orcs, possessing the shortest life span of all the Dark Folk, are also the least understood. They are found in all climates, but prefer to live in mountainous regions. Since their creation, the chaotic evil Orcs have had a reputation for cruelty, violence, irrational rage, hatred of all non-Orc races, and total disregard for anything good or lawful in nature. The history of the Orc race has been one of constant war. All cultures know and fear them outside the comparatively safe confines of city walls. In frontier settings, Orcs are known as fierce and bloodthirsty enemies who attack and harass whenever they can, causing much suffering and loss. In more civilized area, they represent a constant threat, raiding small settlements and caravans, and disappearing long before the local militia can arrive. If humanity were aware of the Orc's ultimate purpose, Orcs would certainly be hunted more than they are now.

Stories abound of the horrible acts perpetrated against mankind. Superstition has it that Orcs were created by a jealous god to bring grief, sorrow, and the eventual end of civilization. The truth is not much different than legend. Orcs were created as a result of jealousy, and they represent a terrible threat to mankind. However, Orcs are not just interested in the extermination of man; they are concerned with the brutal end of ALL non-Orc life everywhere!

The following discussion of Orcs will examine their history, religion, social habits, day-to-day lives, and will serve to give believable motivation to these formidable creatures.

HISTORY AND CREATION

Orc history is the longest of any of the Dark Folk. The Divine Council under the auspices of the God Ethonell, first created the Elves and for a short while there was peace among the gods. The god Osgda soon became jealous of Elthonell's subsequent rise in power from the Elven devotions. Seeking permission from the Divine Council to gain the Knowledge of Creation to create his own race of devotees, Osgda was infuriated when his request was temporarily denied. The Council felt that it would be wise to wait until the Elves had shown themselves to be a viable and productive race before continuing their creative efforts. The Council assured Osgda that when the proper time arrived, he would be given the opportunity to create the next race. Taking this answer as a personal affront, Osgda left the Council chamber in a rage.

During the next several hundred years, Osgda searched the universe endlessly for the secret of creation. Thus, when the Council decided to allow the creation of a second race, Osgda was not to be found. As a result, the Council decided that Toreg Rock Carver (Dwarven Diety; see Book One of the series, DWARVES, for more information), should be allowed to create a new race from the statues he had sculpted. Even as Toreg began his work, Osgda returned and seeing what he thought was treachery, confronted Toreg and demanded that he stop. When Toreg refused, saying that he had the Council's permission, Osgda lost his temper (again!) and attacked Toreg. Osgda was no match for Toreg's great strength and was soundly defeated. Since this time, Osgda and Toreg have been bitter enemies, as have their creations, the Dwarves and the Orcs.

Osgda again appeared before the Council demanding an explanation. While he ranted and raved, a messenger from Toreg arrived and informed the Council of Osga's attack on Toreg. The Council, which had been trying to placate the enraged god, was shocked, and anger overcame reason; the Council banished Osgda from the community of Divine Beings until such time as he apologised for his actions and willingly accepted penance. Osgda, nearly insane with fury, cursed and reviled the Council till he was forcibly ejected from the Council Chambers. He then swore eternal vengeance against the Council and Toreg.

Osgda sought out Elthonell, the creator of the Elves, who had not been present in the Council Chamber. Glibly, Osgda convinced him that the Council had granted him permission to create a new race. Innocently, Elthonell gave the Secret of Creation to him. Alas, creation is not a simple matter even for gods and many of the rituals had been forgotten by Elthonell. As soon as Osgda got what he thought was the complete process, he turned on Elthonell and attempted to strangle the life from him. Rastur, the Sun God, entered the Elf God's Chamber and, seeing the attempted murder, struck Osgda with a bolt of sunfire. Further enraged by his wound and his inability to prevail against the combined might of Elthonell and Rastur, Osgda cursed them both and retreated to the furthest corner of the universe. Not surprisingly, Orcs, since their creation, have regarded both Elves and the Sun as their eternal enemies. While the sun does not effect them directly, Orcs feel that the sun's bright rays are inimical and avoid exposure at all costs. They suffer a -1 attack roll penalty when exposed to bright sunlight.

When Osgda secretly created his race, he formed it in his own image. As you might think, Orcs were imbued with many of his worst qualities. Osgda realized he did not have the ability to give his creatures the long life Elthonell had given the Elves; to compensate, he gave them the ability to reproduce at a prodigious rate. As an afterthought, he granted them the ability to mate with and produce fertile offspring from unrelated species, thus accounting for the preponderance of half-Orc races. In order to increase his strength, Osgda also instilled in his creations a deep seated need to exterminate all non-Orc races.

VITAL STATISTICS

Orcs stand approximately five feet tall with dark reddish-brown skin, long sharp teeth and vicious fangs. They possess normal infravision (30') and are quite at home underground. They have 1d8 for HTK (except for the Warrior Elite and the Chosen who have 1d10). They wear any type of armor and use any weapon available, but prefer to use scimitars, crossbows, and halberds; but a small percentage (15%) will be found using flails and pikes. Orcs, when encountered, usually will be in groups of 5d10 (5% chance of 5d100). For every 50 Orcs, there will be one leader with AC: 0, 5-10d10 HTK (1 on a d6 is 5d10, 2 is 6d10 etc.). There is a 10% chance for an Orc Leader to have a magic weapon and a 20% chance for magic armor. There will also be two Orc Sub-leaders who have 2-4d10 HTK. For every 100 Orcs, there will be one Witchdoctor, AC: 3 HTK: 2-5d10. Each Witchdoctor has a 5% chance of having 1-3 magic items (DM'S choice), and a 25% chance to be accompanied by two assassins, AC: 4 HTK: 1d6.

HABITAT

When Osgda lost his fight with the sun god, he passed his hatred of the sun to the Orcs. As a result, Orcs have always made their homes in deep cavern complexes and mines. Orcs take advantage of any natural tunnels and caverns they find and expand them when overcrowding becomes a problem. Some Orc cities rival Dwarven cities in size (but not in neatness), occasionally extending for miles in all directions.

Orcs are lazy by nature and, where possible, prefer to take rather than make. Applying this philosophy, it becomes obvious that taking an already existing cavern complex away from its owners is preferable to building one —fighting is fun, not work! This attitude has led the Orcs on many wars of conquest against the other subterranean races of the world. Dwarves are constantly prepared for an invasion by Orcs, for they know of the deep-seated Orc hatred of their race; they do not willingly relinquish ownership of the excellent cities they construct.

Due to their highly chaotic nature, Orcs do not utilize plans when extending their cities. As a result, there is very little similarity between one Orc city and another. A typical city consists of a huge maze of tunnels, caverns and rooms which are guaranteed to confuse any non-Orc venturing in. Regardless of precautions taken, anyone wandering about in an Orc city has a 75% chance of becoming lost for every hour they spend within the city confines.

FOOD

Orcs love fresh meat! They are very fond of Dwarf, Elf, Halfling, and Human. Trolls are considered to be an exceptionally fine source of food because of the way they regenerate! Orcs prefer their food to be alive and screaming, but will eat freshly killed if they must. They also eat game animals and other common fare, but this is dictated more by necessity than by preference. Fruits and vegetables, always eaten raw, are not considered decent fare by most Orcs and are used as a last resort against starvation.

Their favorite drink is fermented from a fungus that grows underground in abundance. Flavored with blood, this beverage, called Groog, is nauseating to all other races, and has been known to incapacitate a non-Orc imbiber for 1-4 days.

WEAPONS

Unlike Dwarves, Orcs do not smelt any of the metals found in underground ores preferring to make their weapons and other metal items from refined metals taken in raids.

The favorite weapon of all Orcs is the scimitar. The Orc scimitar, a wicked weapon, measures about 3' long and has the last 8" of the blade serrated like a saw; it does 2-9 (1d8+1) HTK of damage. Other weapons commonly used by Orcs are the halberd, pike, and crossbow. The crossbow is an ideal weapon for Orcs since not much training is required before proficiency is achieved. Halberds suit their temperament admirably and are gleefully used to hack and chop any creatures in their path. The pike, never a favored weapon, has been imposed on them by wise War Chiefs and Overlords.

ORC GUILDS

There are three guilds in Orc society. Guild membership grants an Orc a favored status in the tribe, close to that achieved by the Warrior Elite or The Chosen. About 10% of the total population belong to guilds.

The Guild of Miners

The Orc Miner is, in reality, only an overseer. He does very little mining, but "supervises" the crews of slaves usually Dwarves, Goblins, and Hobgoblins; sometimes even Trolls) who do the actual work. Since the supervisor understands only the rudimentals of good mining

technique, many collapsed chambers and tunnels can be found within the confines of Orc cities.

The Blacksmith's Guild

Orc-forged armor and weapons are of poor-to-fair quality; thus most Orcs prefer to wield captured weapons when they can. Orc blacksmiths receive training and can, if pressed, turn out mediocre weapons and items without help. Whenever possible, Orc blacksmiths use slaves to do the actual work, but this does not improve the quality of the items forged. Orc blacksmiths also turn out cauldrons and kettles, knives, tools, and tips for quarrels and spears. An Orc smithy can forge and temper a scimitar in twenty days divided by the number of slaves in the smithy (round up). A suit of plate mail can be made in 100 days divided by the number of slaves. Each slave can produce ten spear heads or twenty quarrel points per day, but quality suffers greatly.

An Orc smithy is equipped with a forge and foundry and occupied by one Orc Smith, two Orc apprentices, and 1d20 slaves. There is one smithy per hundred inhabitants in any Orc city (round up). It is also likely that there will be an Orc Witchdoctor present to bless all weapons when they are completed.

The Assassin's Guild

Assassins are the most respected class in Orc society. Usually, they serve as the Orc equivalent of a secret police force, acting under the direct control of the Chief, War Chief, or Overlord. Every Orc eventually wants to become an assassin, for the status gained allows them authority over all but the tribal leaders.

Potential Orc assassins are selected from the guilds and the Warrior Elite. They spend years in intense training to learn lock-picking, trap arming and disarming, poisoning, torture techniques, hiding in cover, personal disguise, moving quietly, tracking, climbing, pocket-picking, and weapon skills. They excel at hiding in shadows and natural cover and ambushing adversaries. Skilled in the use of poisons of all types, daggers, bludgeons, garrotes, and torture implements, they (amazingly!) even possess the ability to read! The Orc assassin is also adept in the use of healing herbs used to keep prisoners alive until they can be ransomed or sacrificed.

Those that survive the training achieve a skill level equal to 40% plus his dexterity and half his intelligence (roll 3d6 to determine each). There is a 10% chance that an Orc assassin will have 1-4 of these abilities at 100% (DM's discretion). In addition, an Orc assassin will possess a special ability: Gain Confidence (at 25% plus intelligence). The Gain Confidence ability allows an Orc assassin to convince someone (another Orc or some friendly creature) that he is truly a friend and potential ally. He may attempt this once per person, and only in a non-hostile situation. Once an individual is conviced that the assassin has his best interests at heart, he will remain a friend until the assassin performs an overtly hostile act toward him.

Specializing in stealth, low cunning, and, of course, killing, assassins will occasionally lead parties of Orcs to ambush caravans or raid towns in remote areas where help is far away (for the townsfolk).

WITCHDOCTORS AND MAGIC ITEMS

Orc Witchdoctors, AC: 4-8, HTK: 2-5d10, depending on dexterity, are the tribal healers and magicians. Though they use spells, they wear leather armor and attack as fighters. Orc Witchdoctors may use magic user spells up to third level and clerical spells to the fourth level.

They get their powers directly from Osgda by sacrificing living beings. As a result, they are viewed with fear and mistrust, for Osgda will accept Orcs sacrifices just as readily as anyone/anything else; it is not unusual to find individuals who opposed the Witchdoctor being given the place of honor on the sacrificial altar.

Although the Chief is the spokesman for the tribe, the Tribal Witchdoctor often wields greater power. Few wish to oppose his, or Osgda's demands. The Tribal Witchdoctor selects and assigns new apprentices to other Witchdoctors in the tribe. The apprentice may be of any age, and only the Chief is exempt from being chosen. The apprentices are used for 1-4 years before a determination of their skills is made; those possessing spell-casting talent become assistant Witchdoctors, the others are released. Any Orc may be chosen only once as a potential Witchdoctor; once rejected, he can never be selected again.

Orc Witchdoctors do not have the ability to manufacture major magic items, although they can distill potions of healing that only work on Orcs and brew insinuative and ingestive poisons. They can make luck charms and amulets to ward off minor ills. They also cast spells appropriate to their level, but never cast curative spells. Occasionally, an unusually powerful Witchdoctor is granted the ability to create a magical artifact of limited power. These artifacts are rarely offensive in nature and only work for Orcs. The one exception is the Orc Spear.

THE ORC SPEAR is enchanted so that, when thrown, it will do double damage; it will strike and then return 60' to the wielder. It can also cast a Fire Bolt spell once per day that has a range of 100', never misses and does 4d10 points of damage. The Orc Spear will work for anyone discovering the command word "OSGDA"; however, it will turn the user evil (no save) when the command word is spoken.

THE GREAT PICK, allows its user to excavate earth at double the normal rate for four hours each day.

THE CHARMS OF OSGDA are medallions which give the wearer a 100% Protection from Magic; but whenever a spell is cast within 25', there is a 33% chance for the spell to backfire on its caster. Unfortunately, the charms work erratically and there is a 85% chance for the charm to be non-functional at any given time.

Other charms give protection from various everyday occurances (i.e., warning of poison gas in a new mine, alerting the wearer of the presence of a pitfall, etc.). The particular function of each charm can only be detected by trial and error if an Orc Witchdoctor is not present to identify it.

ORC SOCIAL STRUCTURE

The Family

The Orc lifestyle is similar to that adopted by many other primative cultures. Orcs are born into a family unit dominated by a powerful male and the children are raised by a harem of females until they reach the age of 10 years. Orc families consist of 25-30 individuals; adult males make up roughly half the group and females and young complete the family unit. Ten is considered the age of maturity among Orcs, as their lifespan reaches 55 years only under the best of conditions. A female is considered to be the property of her sire and is subject to his every whim. Usually, the females are married to a male in a family with whom the sire wishes to ally. Once married, the female is then the property of her new husband. A male, once he has reached maturity, is expected to either challenge his sire's supremacy over the family (in a fight to the death), or bow to his authority.

The Clan

The family groups form clans led by the most powerful male in a given area. This is determined each year by a contest of strength; a fight to the death between the current Clan Chief and any challengers. The head of a clan holds the title of Chief and is the military and spiritual leader until defeated.

The Tribe

Ten to twenty clans will often band together into a tribe and will lay claim to a large territory. Tribe leaders are chosen by the most powerful Witchdoctors in the tribe.

Every two years, a special three-day ritual is performed. The Witchdoctors fast and meditate while all the other Orcs celebrate this demonstration of their power. At the end of the ceremony, Osgda sends the Witchdoctors a vision, revealing the identity of the Tribal Chief for the next two years. The Chief is usually the fiercest and smartest Orc Clan Chief. It is a true mark of the evilness of a Tribal Chief, if he can retain his position for more than a single term. Those Chiefs who have this distinction are treated as heros and their fame has spread throughout all Orcdom.

The Orc Nation

Sporadically, Orc tribes will band together under an unusually strong War Chief and form an Orc Nation. During its existence, and Orc Nation is a deadly threat to other human and demi-human races. However, because of their warlike nature, an Orc Nation rarely survives the death of its Overlord. The power struggle resulting from the death of an Overlord invariably leads to civil war among the tribes.

Similar internal wars may be noted at the clan/tribe level when a Chief/War Chief dies, but the effects are not as far-reaching. After a leader's death, the family heads or Chiefs fight for the leadership of the clan or tribe, and the winner takes the title. These fights often result in many deaths, but the clan or tribe stays together.

GOVERNMENT

Orcs are led by the strongest and (usually, but not necessarily) the smartest male. The Overlord, Chiefs and War Chiefs are primarily concerned with the military entanglements of Orc life, leaving the day-to-day functions of government to their appointed "Bullies"—an undisciplined, but loyal group or ruffians; their name reflects the way in which they handle the daily business.

Within the individual social structures, laws change on a moment-by-moment basis since the Bullies are rarely in accord with each other about anything. It is often a wonder that anarchy is as uncommon among Orcs as it is, but despite the unpredictability of the system it does seem to work. Examples of Laws typically pronounced by the Bullies include: not using north and south corridors on certain days, holding Groog mugs (see FOOD, favorite beverage) in the left hand, not the right, females using the right side of corridors, while males use the left, etc. Occasionaly, a Bully will come up with a useful law; when this happens, he is typically voted down by the other

Bullies.

The only common law states that all Orcs must put aside their differences when faced by a common foe. Perhaps this accounts for the otherwise unbelievably stable nature of their culture, since ALL NON-ORCS ARE ENEMIES!

THE DIFFERENT CLASSES OF ORCS

THE WARRIOR ELITE

The most dangerous class of Orcs is the Warrior Elite, which comprises approximately 2% of all male Orcs. The Elite act as the tribe or clan police force and provide guards at the entrances and exits to the Orc cities or towns. Laws ordained by the Bullies are strictly enforced by members of the Orc Warrior Elite. To become one of the Warrior Elite, an Orc must be of unusual size, served in a number of campaigns, and successfully captured prisoners for torture or ransom. Unlike most Orcs, the Elite have 1d10 HTK and usually have maximum (10) HTK.

The Warrior Elite travel in squads of ten and are often accompanied by a 2-3d10 Leader. They normally wear banded mail, carry shields and fight with scimitars (75%) or flails (25%). There is a 50% chance that any given party of Warrior Elite will be riding on Dire Wolves. If this is the case, the Dire Wolves will fight for their riders and should be treated as Warhorses.

Of all the Orcs, only the Warrior Elite can truly be called brave. They will stand fast and face an enemy even if they know it means their death to do so.

The Chosen Subclass

An Orc performing deeds of extreme heroism or exceptional cruelty might come to the attemtion of Osgda himself. Should this happen, Osgda is likely to bestow a

J. CLOUSE '82

special favor on him. This manifests itself as the ability for the Orc to advance in levels of proficiency as would a human character, to a maximum of 11d10. Such an Orc, called one of The Chosen, is a formidable foe indeed! The Chosen are also given an increased lifespan (1d4 years per level) and the ability to function normally in full sunlight. Less than a quarter of the Orcs which have reached a given level within The Chosen are able to reach the next ability level. The Chosen is generally considered to be a subclass of the Warrior Elite.

The Chosen, usually the Leaders and Sub-leaders of the Warrior Elite, are the most likely type to build an Orc Nation. A Chosen will be a Sub-leader until he has 4d10, he will then receive the rank of Leader. An Overlord would be a Chosen with at least 9d10. There will usually be five Chosen in each group of 100 Warrior Elite.

WARRIORS

Like the rest of Orc society, Warriors have 1d8 HTK. Single males usually join the Warriors, preferring the more daring life of a Warrior to the mundane existence of a hunter. Married Orcs may also join the Warriors, but receive less dangerous assignments than their unmarried counterparts. Females may also join, but only if they are of unusual size and strength.

SOLDIERS

Those Orcs who do not qualify to be Warriors and do not want to be hunters or gatherers, must join the Soldiers. These soldiers, usually small, clumsy, and stupid, do not receive thorough training and must use any scaps of armor or weaponry that they can find or steal. Soldiers are often used in large numbers against enemies in order to soften them up prior to a disciplined charge by the Warriors. They are also sent on suicide missions that no one else will take. Any Orc in the Soldiers or the Warriors who sufficiently distinguishes himself will be considered for acceptance in the Elite.

HUNTERS AND GATHERERS

Just above females and young in the tribal pecking order, these Orcs perform the mundane tasks of trapping game, harvesting crops, and gathering roots and fungi. They lead unexciting lives, have low moral values, and almost never engage in combat.

TAKING TOLL

by Les Kay

Introduction for the GM

This adventure is designed for a party of six characters of fourth to seventh level of ability who should have standard armor and weapons. They should also have magic, especially items of a curative nature. Ideally, the party should have two fighters, two spell-casters (clerical and one wizard), one thief, and one multi-classed or unusual character.

The party has recently arrived in Jovian Falls and is seeking employment. They have been approached by a representative of the local merchant's council and invited to attend a meeting to be held that night. (For further details, see player's briefing.)

The merchants are willing to pay more than the 250 gp they initially offer each person, but the party will have to bargain for the extra amount. The most that the merchants are willing to pay is 1,000 gp per person. If the party selects a representative to bargain with Brospero for more money, the negotiation will succeed if the player representing the party rolls a 17 or better on a d20. The representing player may add one to the die roll for each point of Intellect and Appeal above 13 his character has. (NOTE: the odds are weighted in favor of Brospero, as they should should be, for he is one of the most successful merchants in town!) If players attempt to negotiate for higher fees seperately, each player will have only a 5% chance of obtaining the extra amount. Each player may make ONLY ONE ATTEMPT at bargaining for more money. Any successive attempts will fail.

Other Notes

Unless otherwise stated, the corridors in the dungeon are vaulted, with the ceiling 15' overhead at the center, sloping to 8' at the walls. The walls, floors, and ceilings are made of roughly hewn stone. (Add 10% to a thief's chance to climb.) Doors are 6' wide and 8' tall, made of heavy iron bound oak. There are no light sources in the dungeon, except for dimly lit fireplaces. (The Orcs prefer to use infra-vision.) The Orcs have not occupied the dungeon long enough to construct any new traps, so the only traps within the dungeon are in corridors X and Z.

PLAYER'S BRIEFING

You've come to the town of Jovian Falls in search of adventure. You've let it be known that you are available for hire and have been approached by a man named Brospero who states that he is looking for a group of brave adventurers to do some work for them. He invites you to attend tonight's meeting; you agree.

That night, when you reach the meeting place, located in the nobles quarter, you discover that Brospero is one of the town's wealthiest merchants and a member of Duke Borin's personal staff of advisors. Seated at a large table are twelve men who are introduced as the leading merchants of Jovian Falls. Brospero welcomes you and tells you the mission for which you are to be hired.

"Several weeks ago, on the Old East Road near the Old Keep, a band of Orcs set up camp and began to extort money—they call it charging tolls—from merchant caravans and travellers using the road. What we need is a party who can put an end to this deplorable situation and recover the trade goods stolen from their rightful owners. The Duke is indifferent to our request and views this extortion as outside his realm of authority and responsibility, else we would have seen an end to these brigands now. You shall each be paid 250 gp for the task and you may keep any money you find. We only ask you to secure the trade goods the Orcs have stolen from their victims."

GM NOTE: At this point, the party may have questions or may wish to haggle about payment. Once this is finished, they should be allowed to purchase supplies and do anything else necessary for the adventure. Then begin the adventure with the party nearing the point where the Orcs usually ambush their prey. If the party asks about the Old Keep, they will be told it was in ruins when the city of Jovian Falls was first built. Nothing of its history or background is known.

The only other information the council can provide is that the Orcs usually number between 10 and 15 when they waylay the caravans near a large bend in the road. They also know that the Orcs are usually armed with crossbows and halberds. It is believed that there is at least one Witchdoctor with the Orcs, since on at least one occasion when a caravan was stopped, the guards were magically put to sleep.

THE ADVENTURE

ORC STRATEGY

GM ONLY: The Orcs have taken over the Old Keep near the east road in order to obtain gold. They plan to use

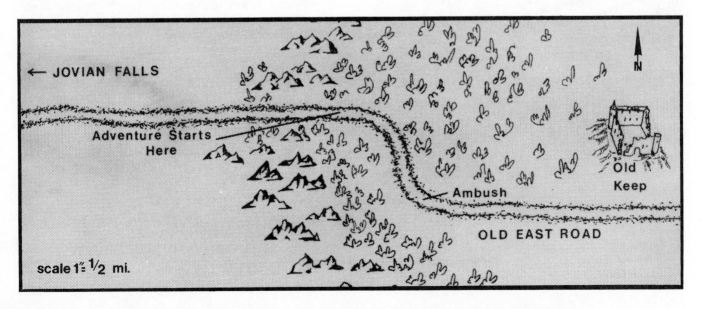

this gold to create a statue of the god Osgda that will occupy a temple that has been newly consecrated to the god. An Orc Witchdoctor convinced the Tribal Chief that it would be appropriate to make the statue of solid gold. Much to his disgruntlement, he was told to accompany the warriors that would be sent to fetch the gold. The Orc Warriors are all Warrior Elite except for the Leader and his two Sub-leaders, who are members of The Chosen.

Currently, the Orcs have amassed nearly enough gold to build the statue. They have also extorted all the trade goods they can carry. They have decided to wait until they have gathered the remaining gold and will then immediately head back to their city in the Black Wyvern Mountains. Naturally, they are on the alert for trouble, not wanting the project to fail at this point, and security is tight. There are only twelve Orcs guarding the road when the adventurers arrive. This encounter should be fairly easy since none of these Orcs own any magic, nor are they backed up by any Dire Wolves.

THE ENCOUNTER AT THE ROAD

The party has arrived at a large bend in the road, about 25 miles from Jovian Falls. It seems likely that this is the spot mentioned by the merchant's council.

GM ONLY: The Orcs have indeed set up their roadblock near the bend in the road. Four Orcs stand guard near trees that have been dropped across the road. The other eight Orcs have been deployed four on each side of the road, with two Orcs on the ground and two in the trees. When the party rounds the bend, they will be told to drop their weapons and toss 50 gp into the trees as a toll. They are told that they are out-numbered, and, if they refuse, they will be killed.

If the party complies, they will be told to pick up their weapons and move on, for they will not be molested. This

is true, for while the Orcs may want to shed human blood, their leader has promised dire consequences if they do anything extreme to enrage the local inhabitants at this point.

If the party opts to fight, they will have to make saving throws vs. spells in order to spot the Orcs hiding in the woods. The Orcs are considered to have the benefit of cover and their AC's reflect this fact. If any of the party members approach the Orcs, reduce the Orcs AC by two points.

Twelve Orcs [AC: 3, HTK: 10 each (1d10), one attack for 2-5 (crossbow) or 2-9 (scimitar)]

Once the Orcs have been killed or captured, the party will see that the road enters a small wooded valley. The Old Keep is clearly visible from the road and cover is sparse between the road and Keep. If any Orcs are captured, they will refuse to give the party ANY information. They will try to escape at every opportunity and will attempt to warn the Orcs at the Keep, even at the expense of their lives.

APPROACHING THE KEEP

The Keep appears to be in a state of extreme disrepair. Even from the road, it is obvious that the walls no longer afford any real protection to anyone in the Keep proper. The front gate has fallen into ruin and there are several breaches in the walls themselves.

The only cover along the way is some sparse brush and a few scraggly trees. If the Keep is approached in daylight, it will be obvious that a guard on the walls would be able to spot the party.

GM ONLY: There are four Orcs on guard inside the walls. If the party approaches during daylight, one of the Orcs will spot them. If the approach is made at night, there is a 58% chance of discovery. If the party uses some special means of concealment, such as invisibility, the chance of discovery is reduced to 10%.

In the event that the party is discovered, the Orcs will have time to prepare a reception. One of the Orcs will be sent to inform the underground troops of the party's approach. He will then return to assist the others with the defense of the walls.

Meanwhile, one of the other Orcs will release the Dire Wolves from their pen in the old stable (Building 8), enabling them to attack the party. The Orcs will then take up positions on the wall facing the direction of the party's approach. They are all armed with crossbows and scimitars.

In the event that the party is not discovered, they will find one Orc on each of the walls of the Keep and the Dire Wolves will be penned in Building 8. There is a 10% chance that the Dire Wolves will detect the party's presence if they approach within 50' of Building 8. Should this occur, the Dire Wolves commence baying and barking to attract the Orc's attention.

10 Dire Wolves [AC: 4, HTK: 22, 24, 18, 11, 21, 13, 30, 16, 19, 18 (4d8); 3 attacks: 1-4x2, 1-6]

4 Orcs [AC: 3, HTK: 10 each (1d10); 1 attack 2-5 (crossbow) or 2-9 (scimitar)]

THE OLD KEEP

1 This is the old entrance to the Keep. The gate has

The Old Keep

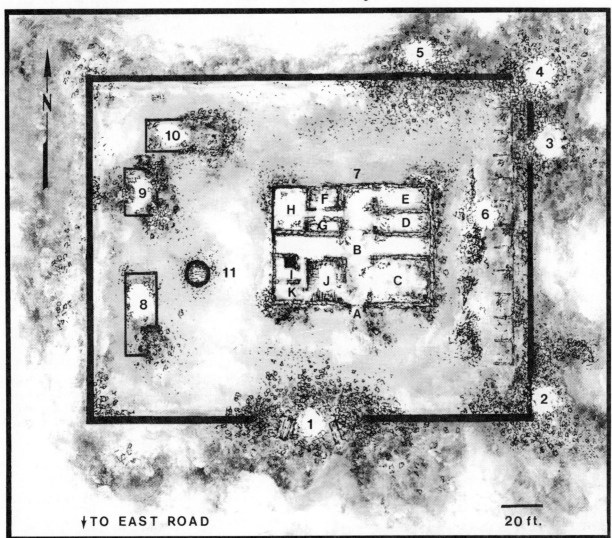

TO EAST ROAD

20 ft.

collapsed wall
intact walls

rubble
trap door

fallen apart and the walls to each side have partially collapsed. There is a great deal of rubble here and the footing is treacherous. (Check twice for each character, roll 5d4 under dexterity or the character has fallen and made noise.)

2-5 In these areas, the wall has collapsed. Point 2 has 5' of the wall still standing. The wall at points 3 and 4 have collapsed to the ground, and point 5 still has 10' of wall standing.

Treat anyone entering the Keep through one of these areas as if they were entering through area 1, but for every 2 feet of wall still standing, there is a plus one to the die roll to see if a person falls or makes a sound (round up).

6 This long row of wooden stalls was once the farmer's market and trading post of the Keep. Over the years, it has fallen in on itself until only the rough outline

of the old stalls remain. There are numerous piles of refuse and rubble scattered along the length of the bazaar, but the area has been searched by the Orcs and there is nothing to be found.

7 This was the Manor House and, like the other structures in the Keep, has fallen to ruin.

8 This is the ruins of the Keep's stables, where the Dire Wolves are now penned (see above).

9-10 These are the ruins of two cottages. When searched, these ruins will only show some signs of being used as shelters (remains of fires, refuse, and clearing of rubble for sleeping space), but there is no evidence of any recent occupation.

11 Well. Its water is drinkable. Otherwise there is nothing in it of special interest.

THE MANOR HOUSE

A   This area was once the main entryway. The broken double doors have suffered from dry rot and the door jamb has partially collapsed.

B   The main hall of the Manor House. It is cross-shaped and runs the length of the building from north to south and east to west. There are no inhabitants in the hall.

C   This was once the main living room of the Manor. There are old scraps of furniture and rubble from the collapsed ceiling in this room. There is nothing of interest in this room.

D   This area was used as servants' quarters and contains nothing of interest.

E   This area also served as servants' quarters. There is nothing of interest here.

F   This was a guest bedroom. If the party spends 30 minutes searching through the rubble, they will find a diamond-studded stickpin worth 700 gp.

G   This area was used as a guest bedroom. A Detect Magic spell will reveal a magical aura on a large piece of fallen masonry. A close examination will reveal a secret compartment. The compartment must be broken open (it will sustain 50 points of damage before breaking) and contains 200 gp, and a magical gem. This is a Gem

of Locking. If the command word is known, the gem, when placed inside a container, will seal the container so that only the person owning the gem may open it. The only other way to open the container is to physically destroy it.

H   This area was also a guest bedroom. By some fluke, the outer walls and ceiling of this room are still intact. The Orcs have searched this room and removed everything of value.

I   This was once a store room used to store foodstuffs. The room is a total wreck. The ceiling has caved in and all of the walls have partially collapsed. Located in the northeast corner of the room, partially camouflaged by timbers, rubble, and dirt is the trap door leading to the dungeon level.

J   The dining hall of the Manor. The ceiling in this room is very unstable. If there is a Dwarf in the party, he will be able to tell that the ceiling will probably collapse if anything is distrubed. If the party enters this room, there is a 40% chance that they will accidently bring down the ceiling doing 5-20 points of damage. This chance should be re-rolled for every minute the party spends in the room.

Under the remains of what might once have been the dining table, there are some broken fragments of crystal. If these are magically mended, they will form a small statue of a beautiful woman. The workmanship is so good that the statue is worth (mended) 350 gp.

K   This area was the kitchen, and is still in good condition, but contains nothing of interest.

THE UNDERGROUND ADVENTURE

GM'S NOTES

By the time the party finds the entrance to the lower level, the Orcs will have had time to make certain arrangements. (In the event that the party is able to capture /kill the guards in the Old Keep before they can alert the defenders below, the GM should bear in mind that the Warrior Elite are a highly organized group and the special strategies outlined below still apply.)

The leader of the Orcs, Rothbardon Brimbite, will be on guard in the treasury (Room 20), along with the Witchdoctor and two Dire Wolves. The two Sub-leaders will be coordinating the Orc defense of the lower levels. While they have not had the time to build any mechanical traps, they have prepared sound defensive strategies.

The Orcs brought along ten Kobold prisoners to do the housekeeping chores and to use as sacrifices to Osgda. They will use these prisoners to cause a diversion (see Room 1) and confuse the party when they enter the dungeon. Then two of the Orcs will attempt to decoy the party into Room 5. Should the party survive, or should the two Orcs fail to lead them to the trap, the remaining Orcs will try to spring the ambush as detailed in the description preceding room ten.

If the party manages to capture one of the Orcs, it will not willingly give any useful information. Unless forced by

J. CLOUSE '82

Dungeon Level

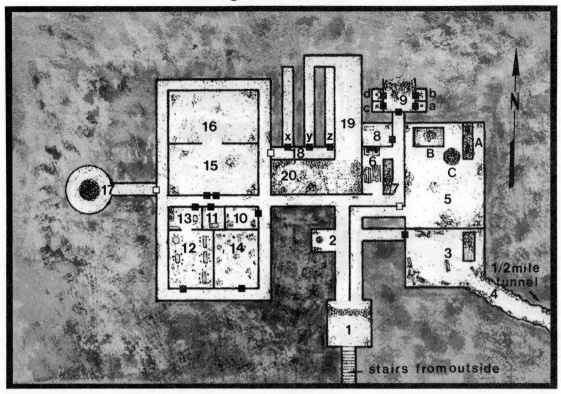

scale: **20 ft.**   door ■   secret door □

magical means, the Orc will not even speak to the party!

1   This is a guard room. It contains no furniture and is completely dark. The Orcs have erected a barricade across the last ten feet of the room in the north. There are six Orcs on guard here, armed with crossbows and halberds. Ten Kobold prisoners are quartered here, and will be used as a diversion.

When the party enters this room, the Kobolds will be armed with short daggers, set free and told that if they can make it to the surface, they can have their freedom! While not especially brave, the Kobolds want their freedom and will attack the party in an attempt to escape.

Four of the Orcs will support the Kobold attack by firing their crossbows at the party. Meanwhile, the other two Orcs will position themselves at the entrance to the tunnel leading to Room 3 and 5. If it looks like the party is about to break through the guards at the barricade, they will make a big show of fleeing down The corridor leading to Room 5. These two will attempt to draw the party to Room 5, where they hope the Pyro-Hydra will finish them off. Naturally, they will attempt to escape through the secret door before the party rounds the corner.

Six Orcs [AC: 3, HTK: 10 each (1d10); 1 attack for
    2-5 points (crossbows), or 1-10 points (halberds)]
Ten Kobolds [AC: 9, HTK: 2, 1, 3, 3, 4, 2, 2, 4, 1, 4
    (1d4); 1 attack for 1-4 (dagger)]

2   This alcove contains a suit of rusty looking plate mail standing on a pedestal. The armor is human-sized and is of a very ancient style. The suit is made of adamantine and is a suit of +2 plate. The Orcs are unaware of its true properties, and think it too old and rusty to bother with! There are two invisible Orcs (see Witchdoctor's spell list) in the northwest and southwest corners of the room. If undiscovered, they will follow the party and attack from behind when the party is ambushed near the entrance to Room 17 (see the description prior to Room 10).
2 Orcs [AC: 3, HTK: 10 each (1d10); 1 attack for 1-10
    (halberds)]

3   This is the lair of Andromedeus the Androsphinx. The room was once the armory for the Keep. There are numerous racks, once used to store weapons, scattered about the room, but no weapons will be found in the room. Andromedeus has had several encounters with the Orcs who sought to take his treasure. He subdued the Orcs with riddling contests (and roaring). Since then, the Orcs have decided to leave Andromedeus and his treasure trove alone! Andromedeus is easy-going by nature and prone to asking riddles rather than fighting. He is always looking for new and interesting riddles; if a party member supplies him with one he likes (GM's option) he will reward them with a small gem.

Andromedeus' treasure consists of 482 cp, 651 sp, 190 gp, 27 pp, 1189 gp in jewelry, and a Staff of Striking.

Andromedeus the Androsphinx [AC: -2, HTK: 48 (12d8); 2 attacks for 2-12 plus roar]

4   This area is an old escape tunnel. It meanders underground and eventually exits about 3/4 of a mile from the Keep in dense woods. Andromedeus uses the tunnel.

5   The Keep's weaponsmith once worked here. There are indications of its former use still to be found here. In the northeast corner of the room is the old forge (A) that was used to heat metal. In the northwest corner is the sand pit (B), and south of these is the water bath (C) used to temper blades and other metal-work.

    This room is now the lair of a female Pyro-Hydra and her clutch of eggs. She is using the sand pit as a nest and has stored her treasure trove in the old forge. The Orcs have tried to relieve her of her treasure, but after the first ten were roasted alive, they decided that perhaps she should be left alone! As a result of these attempts, she is in a bad humor and will breathe fire immediately at anyone who enters the room. The Orcs will try to lure invaders to her lair and allow her to dispose of them

    The Hydra's treasure consists of 1,600 sp, 420 gp, and a ring that lowers its wearer's armor class by two points. There are also five eggs in the sand pit worth about 500 gp each in a large city. The eggs will hatch in about three weeks and require very gentle handling to prevent breakage.
    Pyro-Hydra [AC: 5, HTK: 72 (9d8), 9 attacks for 1-8 points (one per head) plus breath weapon for 8 points per head, twice per day/head]

6   The Orcs use this room for recreation. They have set up two long tables with benches in the center of the room. There is a fire-burning in a fireplace on the north wall of the room. A loose brick in the fireplace conceals a small leather pouch that contains a platinum broach worth 100 gp.

7   This collapsed stairway used to lead to the second level. The stairway is completely impassable and any attempt to excavate it is likely to cause more material to collapse.

8   This is a bedroom, used by the two Orc Sub-leaders. There are two unkempt beds and two unlocked chests in the room. The chests contain filthy clothing and worn boots. The room is unoccupied.

9   This room was once a private library and trophy room. Over the years, part of the north wall has collapsed and only 25'-30' of the room remain. The doors lead to 10'x10' chambers where the trophies were kept.
    A   This chamber contains the rotten remains of a giant stag.
    B   This chamber contains only a pedestal, upon which lies a shriveled pile of dried skin.
    C   This chamber contains the well-preserved remains of a Harpy poised as if in flight. If a spell to Detect Magic is cast, it will reveal that the Harpy is magical. This is a result of the powerful preserving spell that was cast to insure that the Harpy would not decay.
    D   This chamber contains a stuffed Mind Flayer mounted on a pedestal of solid silver. There are also six freshly killed Orc corpses in the room.

        The pedestal and statue are protected by a Warding spell that will do 3-18 of damage to anyone that tries to steal either item. A Detect Magic spell will not reveal the presence of this ward. The spell will work only once per day, but will affect everyone in the room (roll seperate damage for each person; a save vs. magic halves damage).

IMPORTANT!
READ THIS SECTION BEFORE CONTINUING TO ANY OTHER ROOM IN THIS SECTION OF THE DUNGEON

If the party has gotten past (or avoided) the Kobolds, the Sphynx, and the Hydra, the Orcs have a deadly trap set. This is an all or nothing attempt to stop any invaders and the Orcs will be desperate to succeed.

Six Orcs, armed with crossbows and scimitars, are positioned in the hall near the door to Room 11. When the party reaches the four-way intersection, these Orcs will begin firing and dropping back toward the T-intersection near the secret door to Room 17. The remaining 18 Orcs, including the two Sub-leaders, are divided into three groups. The first group is stationed in the corridor north of Room 17 (near the T-intersection), the second group is south of the T-intersection, and the third group is in the most corridor, near the door to Room 14. When the party closes with the six Orcs firing on them, they will be drawn into the trap!

The six Orcs will retreat to the T-intersection, where they, along with the other two groups lead by the two Sub-leaders, will engage the party in melee. Meanwhile, the third group will circle behind the adventurers and attack.

Additionally, the two invisible Orcs from Room 2 will, if they haven't already been dealt with by the party, strike at the party from the rear.
Six Orcs [AC: 4, HTK: 10 each (1d10); 1 attack for 2-5 (crossbow) or 2-9 (scimitar)]
Group 1:
    Orc Sub-leader [AC: 3, HTK: 19 (2d10), 1 attack for 2-9 (scimitar)]
    5 Orcs [AC: 4, HTK: 10 each (1d10), 1 attack for 2-9]
Group 2
    3 Orcs [AC: 4, HTK: 10 each (1d10), 1 attack for 2-9]
Group 3
    Orc Sub-leader [AC: 1, HTK: 29 (3d10), 1 attack for 2-9 (scimitar), +1 plate mail, Charm of Osgda]
    8 Orcs [AC: 4, HTK: 10 each (1d10), 1 attack for 2-9]

10 This is the Orc Witchdoctor's bedroom. There is a small wooden shrine to Osgda in the southeast corner of the room. In the Southwest corner is a pile of expensive furs that the Witchdoctor sleeps on. Next to the pile is a small jeweled chest with a handle in the shape of a mouth. The chest is trapped such that, when opened, the lips will slam shut cutting off any fingers between them. Inside the chest is a +2 dagger, a jeweled necklace worth 1200 gp, a leather bag with 30 pp, and

a single diamond worth 400 gp.

11 This is the Orc leader's room. The only article of furniture is a bed on the south wall. Under the bed is a small sack tied shut with copper wire. Inside the sack are a set of seven ivory figurines. The figurines are carved to look like people dressed in rich garments. Because of their fine workmanship, the set is worth 1000 gp. Individually, the pieces are worth only 100 gp.

12 This room is used as a mess hall. There are several wooden tables and numerous chairs in the room. The floor is littered with the bones of small humanoids.

13 This is used as a small kitchen. It is not currently occupied.

14 This is a barracks used by the Orcs. Piles of moth-eaten furs on the floor are used by the Orcs for sleeping. Scattered about the room are 10 burlap sacks; they contain old, dirty clothes, worn boots, old belts, etc., (nothing of value).

15-16 These two rooms are used by the Orcs to hold their remaining Kobold slaves. The rooms have straw-covered floors and contain 9 Kobolds [AC: 7, HTK: 2 each (1d4)]. These Kobolds have been starved and cruelly treated. If questioned, they will say that they will gladly help the party fight the Orcs if the party will arm them. If the party does arm the Kobolds, they will attempt to use the weapons to fight their way to freedom.

17 The Orcs are unaware of the secret door leading to this room. The party must apply 42 strength points pushing on the left side to open the door. Up to three people may push on the door at one time. The room contains a 30' well that dried up years before the Keep was abandoned. The first occupants of the complex, later killed by the plague, buried a chest containing 1200 gp, 200 ep, 200 pp, 1500 gp in gems and jewelry, a vorpal longsword, and a suit of +2 chainmail at the bottom of the well.

18 There are three doorways on the north wall of the hall, each leading to a long corridor. There is a Permanent Illusion in each of these three corridors that make them appear identical. They all seem to be 50' long with a door at the far end.

Corridors X and Z are traps. When the party enters either of these corridors, the door will slam shut behind them and can only be opened by magical means. It will take a Dispel Magic and a Knock spell to open these doors once they have locked. Once locked, the doors cannot be opened from the outside.

Once the door to corridor X has closed, the corridor will begin to fill with water from ducts located in the north end of the corridor, above the illusionary door. It will take one full turn for the room to fill with water. The door to this room is enchanted and can take 75 points of damage before being destroyed.

When the door to corridor Z shuts, the corridor will begin to fill with sand. The sand enters the room through numerous small openings running the length of the ceiling. It will take one full turn for the room to completely fill with sand, smothering the people trapped inside. The door to this room can withstand 100 points of damage.

Corridor Y leads to Hall 19. THERE IS NO TRAP IN THIS CORRIDOR, BUT THE ILLUSIONARY DOOR WILL RESIST ALL ATTEMPTS TO OPEN IT. In order to pass the door, the party must successfully disbelieve in the illusion, or dispel it.

19 This long hall will test the nerve of anyone passing through it. Whenever anyone walks along the hall, a percentile dice should be rolled for each segment. If the roll is 5% or less, a crossbow bolt (from a small slit in the wall) will randomly hit a party member for 2-5 points of damage; otherwise, the bolt will narrowly miss a party member. This onslaught of bolts will continue as long as someone remains in the hall.

20 This room is used by the Orc captain as the treasury. The room is lined with green tinted marble and there is a multi-colored mosaic on the floor depicting a martial scene. There are numerous bags in the room that contain furs, spices, statuary, books, and 9,953 gp. These are the trade goods and tolls that the Orcs have been extorting from merchants and travellers. The room is guarded by the Orc Captain, the Orc Witchdoctor, and three Dire Wolves.

Orc Captain [AC: 0 (+3 plate), HTK: 52 (6d10), 2 attacks for 3-13 (+2 halberd)]

Orc Witchdoctor [AC: 5, HTK: 29 (5d8), 1 attack for 1-6 (staff)]; Spells: (Magic User) Magic Missile, Charm Person, Burning Hands, Shield, Sleep, Knock, Invisibility, Mirror Image, Lightning Bolt; (Clerical) Cause Wounds (3), Sanctuary, Spirit Hammer, Dispel Magic]

Dire Wolves [AC: 4, HTK: 28, 16, 30, 31 (4d8), 3 attacks for 1-4. 1-4. 1-6]

GNOLLS

by Arthur Miller and Irwin Goldstein

Gnolls are a race of large fierce humanoids with hyena-like heads and jaws and short blunt nails on their hands and feet. They are covered with short, dirty looking fur ranging from black to brown in coloration. Males range in height from 7 to 8½ feet, while females range from 6½ to 8 feet. Gnolls usually live above the ground and as a result do not have infravision. A typical Gnoll is of average intelligence and chaotic-evil in alignment.

Gnolls have from 2d8 to 5d8 HTK as described below. They wear fur, leather, or splint armor, and often carry shields, thus giving them an armor class of 4, 5, or 6. For weapons, Gnolls favor longbows, spears, and swords, though it is not uncommon for other weapons to be used. They receive a +2 damage bonus due to their strength. If unarmed, they will attack with hands or teeth, doing 1d4 HTK of damage for each hand and 2d4 HTK damage with a bite.

Gnolls will typically be encountered in groups of 10d20 in a raiding party, and 20d20 in a permanent settlement. When encountered in a raiding party, there will be one war leader of 3d8 HTK for every 30 Gnolls and one war leader of 4d8 HTK for every 60 Gnolls. There will also be one Witchdoctor of 1st-3rd level for every 60 Gnolls, and one Witchdoctor of 4th-5th level for every 90 Gnolls. If there are over 150 Gnolls in a raiding party, a Chieftain of 5d8 HTK and a 7th level Shaman will also be present.

In a permanent Gnoll settlement, there will always be a Chieftain of 5d8 HTK with 1d4+1 bodyguards of 4d8 HTK. There will also be at least one Shaman of 4th-7th level and at least one Witchdoctor of 2nd-5th level.

If there are 100-200 Gnolls, the Tribal Shaman will be of at least 5th level and he will have 1d4 assistants. The Tribal Witchdoctor in this case will be no lower than 3rd level with 1d2 assistants.

If there are 201-300 Gnolls, the Tribal Shaman will be at least 6th level and have 1d4+1 assistants. Also, the Tribal Witchdoctor will be at least 4th level with 1d4 assistants.

If there are 301-400 Gnolls, the Tribal Shaman will be 7th level and he will have 1d4+4 assistants. The Tribal Witchdoctor in this case will be 5th level and have 1d4+1 assistants.

All Chieftains, War Leaders, Shamans, and Witchdoctors are in addition to the number of Gnolls indicated by the dice. In a settlement, there will also be females equal in number to 30% of the males, and children under 12 equal in number to 100% of the males.

TRIBAL LIVING

The tribe is the basic unit of Gnoll life, and no Gnoll would consider life outside of the tribe. Tribal life is organized in an attempt to reach a balance between the Gnolls' pack drive and the need for inviolate areas of individuality and privacy.

Most Gnoll activities are communal: war, hunting, eating, etc. Villages and settlements are set up around the common area, which always contains the eating area. No Gnoll would ever eat alone when in a settlement.

While the tribes are constant, they are not static. Individuals and families are constantly leaving one tribe and joining another. This fact may explain one of the most puzzling aspects of Gnoll life. Despite their warlike and bloody nature, and the constant fighting among individual Gnolls, no Gnoll tribe has ever been known to go to war with another Gnoll tribe.

Every Gnoll tribe is divided into three parts: children, unmarried males, and families. Gnolls up to the age of twelve are considered children and have no responsibilities. Children are taught what they need to know to survive, but are otherwise allowed to enjoy themselves. They are guarded and loved by the entire tribe. Almost any adult Gnoll would die to save a child (+3 to hit, -3 to AC).

At the age of twelve, females are forced to either marry or join another tribe. Any tribe that she may join will expect her to marry within six months or face expulsion. Females not married by their thirteenth birthday are summarily sacrificed. Males are sent to the barracks for unmarried males. They may also leave for another tribe if they wish, but they will still end up in the male barracks.

The unmarried males are the defenders and warriors of the tribe. They also make up the raiding parties which attack villages and caravans. Almost every community keeps slaves to do the heavy and dirty work, and for use as blood sacrifices. They are also a potential source of food, but they are seldom eaten, as they are too valuable. Slaves are the communal property of the tribe.

HOME LIFE

Little is known about Gnoll home life, since the only way for an outsider to enter an occupied Gnoll home is to kill every member of the family, down to the smallest child. Obviously, this limits research opportunities.

Some things, however have been determined. The family unit usually consists of one male, one female, and two to four children. The Gnoll home is usually close and dark with several partitions for sleeping. The houses are strongly built and usually covered with earth. Each Gnoll keeps his personal weapons, treasures, and other personal possessions in the family area. They try to hide or lock away their valuables in order to protect them from intruders.

COURTSHIP, MARRIAGE, AND THE RELATIONSHIP BETWEEN THE SEXES

Courtship among the Gnolls is almost completely controlled by the females. When a female reaches marriageable age, the unmarried males who are proven warriors compete for her favors. Since males outnumber females by three to one, wives are greatly desired, and the competition is keen. The female is free to choose whomever she wishes. Any Gnoll who tries to force a female's choice will end up having every unmarried male, and possibly the entire tribe, trying to kill him. The only restrictions on the female's choice of a mate are that he must be a proven, unmarried warrior and that she must marry within six months of becoming available (or leave the tribe).

The marriage ceremony is simple, ending with a blood sacrifice to seal it, followed by a celebration. The new husband is immune to any challenge for at least a full moon following the marriage. This is done to decrease the chance of another male killing him out of jealousy. If a male Gnoll does kill a married male (after the period of immunity), he may claim his victim's belongings, but not his wife. These fights only make another female available; the challenger has no claim on her. As always, she is free to choose her own new mate, and has six months to do so. If the female Gnoll is killed or wounded during the fight, the would-be challenger is immediately set upon by all other Gnoll males. His death is slow and deliberately painful.

Because there are so few females, they are treated with more respect than outsiders might expect. Not only does the female get to choose her mate, but she is also able to divorce him and re-marry whenever she chooses. This results in her being constantly courted by most of the unmarried males of the tribe.

FOOD

The Gnolls are primarily, though not exclusively, carnivorous. Little of the animal is allowed to go to waste, even the blood of their prey is consumed. Moreover, they also supplement their diet with fish, berries, nuts, and other edible wild plants. They make a strong drink of fermented

fruit juices and honey. While they have herd animals, usually pigs and goats, they have never turned to planting and harvesting crops. They combine hunting, fighting, foraging, and herding to provide themselves with sufficient food. Meat is usually eaten raw, except when preserving it for future consumption. Human meat is one of the Gnolls' favorite foods, and they also enjoy eating other humanoid races, though they detest the taste of dwarves.

PETS

Gnolls keep a wide variety of pets, ranging from such mundane creatures as wild dogs and hyenas to stirges and huge spiders. In most cases, pets are trained as hunting animals and will often accompany Gnolls on raiding and foraging expeditions.

ILLNESS AND HEALING

Gnolls are subject to the normal range of accidents and diseases. Treatment and healing are in the hands of two groups: the females and the Shamans. Only the Shamans can perform magical healing, but both groups have an extensive knowledge of medicinal plants and herbs and some knowledge of crude surgery techniques. Gnolls have been known to use healing potions obtained either in trade (often from Trolls) or by war. Some 7th level Gnoll Shamans can also manufacture healing potions.

GNOLL BIOLOGY

Gnolls have an average lifespan of seventy years. The females become fertile at age twelve and remain fertile until death. The have a six month gestation period. The newborn are helpless for the first six months of life but soon begin to exhibit a sense of curiosity. For these first six months, the Gnoll babies have soft, fluffy white fur. Some merchants prize this fur highly and will pay up to 200 gp per pelt.

RELIGION

The Gnollish religion seems strange to outsiders but it is very logical considering the nature of Gnolls. They worship the demon/god Xyrmgnollven, but their attitude often seems less like worship than a mutually agreed upon contract necessary to the survival of both the race and the god.

The Gnolls claim to know how their race was created. They believe that, sometime in the far distant past, Xyrmgnollven watched the various gods create races of worshippers and grow more powerful as a result. He realized that unless he did something soon, he would be overwhelmed by his enemies. He tried to obtain the secret of creation from the other gods, but none of them would part with this great secret. Xyrmgnollven refused to be stopped. After careful thought and much preparation, he trapped alive a pack of hyenas and an equal number of bears. Through magic and bloody surgery, he combined them into beings who looked much like him. He could make them move, eat, and obey orders, but they were not alive. In desperation, he infused his own blood into each of his creations and, slowly, they came alive. Gnolls consider themselves descended from Xyrmgnollven, and by their own view, part god.

This legend determines the nature of Gnollish religion. The Gnolls repay their god's blood sacrifice with other blood sacrifices and, in return, their god protects and strengthens them. Gnoll sacrifices range from animals to the various intelligent races, with human sacrifices being the most prized. When asking Xyrmgnollven for a special favor, it is not unusual for a Gnoll to burn a cup of its own blood.

Gnolls worship no other gods, for none are necessary. After all, their god is not overly demanding and understands their needs and ways. In addition, they greatly enjoy the sacrificial services.

The services consist of slowly draining the blood from a living sacrifice into a burning fire as the Witchdoctor prays to Xyrmgnollven. After the sacrifice dies, it is eaten. The Gnolls abhor waste.

The religion is administered by the Shamans. Gnoll Shamans are those who can most easily communicate with the god. They conduct the blood sacrifices of the captives and condemned Gnolls. It is to the Shamans that the god gives his powers and his knowledge. He gives them their clerical spells. Gnoll Shamans can rise to the 7th level of clerical ability. They receive 1d8 HTK per level.

After death, the Gnolls expect to join Xyrmgnollven for an eternity of bloodletting, war, hunting, and celebration.

XYRMGNOLLVEN

AC: -4
HTK: 200
Stats: 23, 20, 20, 21, 20, 22

Xyrmgnollven usually materializes on this plane as a 10' tall Gnoll with coal black fur, blood red eyes, and greenish-yellow teeth. He regenerates at the rate of 3 HTK per melee round. Xyrmgnollven usually wears a suit of +4 ring mail, carries a +3 shield, and weilds a +3 bastard sword. Xyrmgnollven has 11th level clerical abilities, 9th level magic user abilities and fights as a 20th level fighter. In addition, he has all normal demon abilities. The darkness he can cause is of a 15' radius. He can gate once per day with a 95% chance of success (50% Type III, 30% Type IV, 15% Type V, 5% Type VII). [Attacks: 1 (2d4+14)]

LAW, JUSTICE, AND GOVERNMENT

In Gnoll society, law is simple, justice is unlikely, and government is confusion.

First of all, there are no formal written laws, just tribal customs which amount to nearly the same thing. Several of these customs have already been covered under courtship and marriage. There are two other customs: No Gnoll may endanger the tribe, and no adult may kill or cripple a child. There are no other fixed customs. They have only one punishment for law breakers—death as a blood sacrifice to their god Xyrmgnollven.

The Tribal Witchdoctor is the arbiter of Gnoll justice. If there is some doubt as to the guilt of a Gnoll, the Witchdoctor prepares two cups of blood, one poisoned. The accused Gnoll is then allowed to pick a cup and the accuser must take the other. Simultaneously, the accused and the accuser quaff the contents of their cups. Obviously, the Gnoll that survives is the one telling the truth!

Government, as we understand it, does not exist. The leader of a group is simply the one with the most influence. This can vary, not only from day to day, but also from decision to decision. Depending on the situation, successful warriors, hunters, or traders are consulted for their opinion. Fierce arguements are common over any decision, and fights to the death have been observed over whether or not it was too wet to go deer hunting. The only general rule seems to be that NO ONE GIVES ORDERS TO A GNOLL, ONLY SUGGESTIONS!

There is, however, an exception to this rule! Whenever a new settlement is built, or an old Chieftain dies, the tribe holds a contest (rarely to the death) to select a new Chief. The Chief is responsible for protecting the settlement and any orders concerning this subject are obeyed by all other Gnolls. Any who disobey the Chieftain are judged guilty of endangering the tribe and treated appropriately.

RELATIONSHIPS WITH OTHER RACES

Gnolls often maintain cordial relations with the other Dark Races, especially Trolls. Gnoll mercenaries often serve in the forces of various Dark Races, but the Gnolls seldom hire other races as mercenaries. When they do hire mercenaries, they hire Trolls, for Trolls are the race they respect the most.

Despite this, Gnolls consider every race to be their legitimate prey. As a result, all other races view them with more than a little suspicion. Due to what they believe is their heritage, Gnolls feel superior to all the other races, and this makes them even less popular among the Dark Folk.

MAGIC

There are only three sources of magic in Gnoll society: Witchdoctors, Shamans, and items stolen from other races. Since the Witchdoctors learn their spells from their god, they do not keep magic books (though they can use both books and scrolls). Magic items are rare and greatly prized, and usually only a Leader, Shaman, or Witchdoctor will have one. Any magic items which the Gnolls cannot use, they trade away. Gnoll Witchdoctors can rise to 5th level

magic user ability. Unlike other magic users, Gnoll Witchdoctors receive 1d8 HTK per level.

ARTIFACTS

The only known Gnoll artifact is an oddly shaped knife which the Gnolls claim was used to create their race. When the Archmage Qandraas managed to steal it (about 2,000 years ago), he discovered some of its properties. Before the entire Gnoll race hunted him down and killed him and all his retainers, Qandraas managed to leave a record of his researches.

The knife has a curved blade about one and one-half feet long made of some unknown metal. About six inches of the back of the blade is serrated. Both blade and hilt are unornamented except for runes on the blade. Qandraas found himself unable to mark or damage this blade in any way. Living flesh presented no resistance to the knife and it cut through bones as if they were made of cheese. Conversely, the handle heals any wound with a touch. The blade will bend and twist to conform its shape to its user's desires. His last discovery was that any Gnoll within ten feet of the blade cannot be killed!

The Knife of Xyrmgnollven is apparently held by the Gnolls at present, but its location is unknown.

TRADE AND CRAFTS

The Gnolls engage in trade on a regular basis. Most of their trade is with the other Dark Races. They trade cheeses, furs, herbs, and iron weapons, for food, potions, iron ore, and slaves.

The Gnoll skill at metal working is comparable to that of humans living in the Iron Age. Gnolls are just beginning to learn how to make steel. Their metalwork is plain and without ornamentation, but it is sturdy and able to withstand much heavy use.

WEDDING SACRIFICE

by Irwin Goldstein

The following is an adventure designed specifically with Gnolls in mind. Within the adventure can be found many examples of the ideas expressed in the foregoing presentation about Gnolls. This adventure is recommended for a party of from six to ten adventurers ranging in level from third through sixth. The party should be well balanced between fighters and spell-casters, and ideally should contain at least one thief and one ranger. If these characters do not exist among your group of players, then non-players can be easily introduced into the adventure as outlined in the introduction which follows.

ADVENTURE BACKGROUND

FOR THE DM: The party is currently staying in the town of Jovian Delta. (See the main continental map.) It is up to you to get the players to this point in order for the adventure to begin. One way you might attract your players to this town is to have them hired as caravan guards by some merchant travelling to Jovian Delta. The merchant will tell of increased Gnoll activity in the area, thus explaining the need for extra guards. Have the merchant pay the players just enought to get them to go along.

Jovian Delta, named for its proximity to the mouth of the Jovian River, is a large walled city with a population of about twelve thousand. Its position near the Jovian River makes Jovian Delta the largest trade center of Mamaryl. In addition, the town is also home to many fishermen. Thus, seafood is one of Jovian Delta's main exports.

Jovian Delta is governed by an elected council of twelve elders who serve for life once elected. The elders, when needed, elect the leader of the town council. Jovian Delta's current leading elder is an old warrior named Artemo Myskip. About twenty years ago, Myskip was involved in driving off a group of bandits who were terrorizing one of the roads leading to Jovian Delta. His success in these battles against the bandits earned him much respect in town, and he was soon elected to the council of elders. Since that time, the leading elder died and Myskip was elected as the town's new leader. Myskip has one daughter, Yolanda, who is a magic-user. Yolanda's mother died several years ago of natural causes. Yolanda is also much respected by the people of Jovian Delta, and is expected to be elected to the council of elders some day.

The following is a background to be given to the players after they have spent some time in town.

FOR THE PLAYERS: While spending some time in the town of Jovian Delta, you have discovered that a small army is being gathered together to increase patrols along the road and find the Gnolls' current lair. The town's leader, Artemo Myskip, is currently out of town with his daughter Yolanda, but they are due back tomorrow. Although Artemo is old and therefore of little value as a warrior, his judgement is respected and the army will wait for his return before deciding on a final plan of attack.

That night, a little after dinner, you are sitting in a local tavern relaxing. Suddenly a loud commotion is heard from the streets. Running out to see what is going on, you see a large crowd following a horse being led by a rather battered-looking soldier. On the horse rides an injured old man. The crowd proceeds to the central market place where several town leaders rush to greet the old man. From others in the crowd, you are able to pick up that the old man is the town's leader Myskip, and the soldier is one of his bodyguards. Myskip is taken from the horse and laid on the ground while a cleric from the town's main temple begins chanting Cure spells and binding his wound. The crowd quiets as the soldier explains what happened:

"We were just a half day's ride out of town, almost past the swamp when our party was ambushed by Gnolls. There were so many of them, and on all sides. We fought as best we could, and with the help of Yolanda's spells, we nearly all survived. But then more Gnolls arrived, and with them came a Gnoll not dressed in battle armor, but in strange robes and carrying a crude staff. He did some sort of spell, and suddenly Yolanda could no longer speak her spells. That was the turning point of the battle. The Gnolls overwhelmed Yolanda's guards and, I think, took her alive. Since the Gnolls were concentrating on her, I was able to get Myskip out of danger. The other guards remained behind to cover our escape and are probably all dead."

The guard had been speaking in a strained and shaking voice, but now he collapses to the ground, sobbing. Some nearby clerics tend to his wounds. Meanwhile, Myskip's wounds have been healed, and he begins speaking with the other town leaders. They tell him of their plans to send an army looking for the Gnolls. After some hushed discussion, Myskip addresses the crowd.

"An army is being gathered to rid our town of the Gnollish threat, but it will not be ready for several days. My daughter has been taken alive by the Gnolls. No doubt, they intend to offer her as a blood sacrifice to their evil god. Therefore, I am offering to pay 20,000 gp to the group of adventurers that returns my daughter safely to me. Any interested groups should come to the town hall immediately!"

The crowd disperses while Myskip and the other leaders head for the town hall.

FOR THE DM: At this point, the players will hopefully go to the town hall to offer their services. If you wish to introduce any non-player characters into the adventure, this is a good point to do so. Simply make them other adventurers who have come to the town hall to offer to help rescue Yolanda. At this point, you may also wish to increase or decrease the reward offered, depending upon the economy of your campaign.

FOR THE PLAYERS: Your party has gathered at the town hall to offer your services. You are shown into a large room with a long table. The town's leaders are seated at the table with Myskip at the head. Myskip speaks. "I thank you all for coming. We have little time, so I will speak directly of the matter at hand. I have had my bodyguard draw a map which will lead you to the location of the ambush. It should not be very difficult for you to track the attack party back to the Gnoll settlement if you leave tomorrow morning. If there is anything else we can provide you with in the way of equipment, you need but ask and it will be yours."

FOR THE DM: You may or may not want to grant requests for magic items at this point depending on the strength of your party. Once all request for equipment, etc. have been worked out, Myskip will speak once more to the party:

FOR THE PLAYERS: Myskip gives you some final advice: "The Gnollish stronghold is undoubtedly somewhere in the swamp. The road past the swamp is relatively safe (or at least it has been until recently), but the swamp itself contains many dangers. In addition to deep bogs and quicksand, many deadly creatures (aside from the Gnolls) inhabit the swamp. I do not expect you to be able to rush in and kill all the Gnolls of the swamp, and this should not be your approach. The little we know of the Gnolls tells us that they probably live in several small settlements throughout the swamp. All I ask is that you

find where my daughter is being held, rescue her, and bring her back alive.

"I have done all that I can to prepare you. Please go now and rest for the night if you feel it is necessary, but leave no later than sunrise! Good luck and may the gods go with you!"

FOR THE DM: Here is the background from the Gnoll's point of view:

Gnolls have lived in the southern part of the Jovian swamp for many years. Living in a desolate area, the village rapidly grew and recently had to face an overpopulation problem. As a result, some of the village's greatest warriors went north to start a new settlement. After finding a suitable island, the Gnolls set about fortifying it and making it suitable for habitation. While the new town was being built, the founding Gnoll warriors held a competition to choose the town's new Chieftain. The town has now been completed, and, as a final step, the new Chieftain has to take a wife. The usual Gnollish courtship began between the new Chieftain and one of the old Chieftain's daughters. She finally accepted and the wedding ceremony was planned to take place in the new town. The Gnoll Shamans decided that for such an important wedding, only a very special blood sacrifice would suffice. Therefore, they set out to find a human sacrifice.

Eagerly, the Gnolls watched the road through the swamp for a choice victim. When Myskip and Yolanda happened along, the Gnolls attacked. At first, the Shaman leading the expedition held back, thinking the Gnoll warriors could easily overwhelm the defenders. As the defenders fought back the Gnolls, the Shaman summoned his guards, stepped forth and cast a Silence spell on Yolanda. A young human maiden magic-user would make the perfect sacrifice!

Through the determined effort of his guards, Myskip and an injured guard were able to escape alive. All humans protecting their escape were slain after a prolonged battle. Now the Gnolls would have much human meat for the wedding feast!

The Gnolls have notified the Chief that a suitable sacrifice has been found and now await the arrival of the bride and her party. The wedding ceremony will take place three nights from the night Yolanda was captured. At exactly midnight, she will be sacrificed to sanctify the marriage!

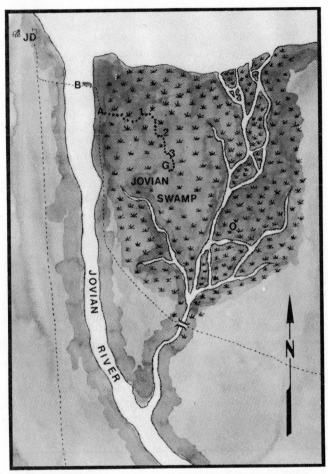

scale **2 mi**

JD Jovian Delta   **1,2,3** Trap sites

B   Barge Crossing   Road

A   Ambush site   Bridge

G   Gnoll village   Gnoll tracks

O   Old Gnoll village

SWAMP TRAPS

The map of the Jovian Swamp shows the location of the ambush site and the Gnoll villages. The village marked with a "G" is the new Gnoll village, while the "O" represents the older Gnoll village. The dotted line leading from the ambush site to the new village is not truly a path, but a relatively safe route through the swamp. This is the path the Gnolls took, and if there is a ranger with the party, he should have little trouble following.

Movement in the swamp while on the path is at the rate of 1½ miles per hour on foot. It is not possible to ride horses in the swamp. The party should have enough time to arrive early on the wedding day, but if they waste time in the swamp, they may arrive later. Movement in the swamp when off the path is at the rate of ½ mile per hour.

The Gnolls suspected that someone might attempt to track them down, so they set several traps along the way to their village. Each trap is marked with a number on the map and is described below:

TRAP 1: The Gnolls have set up three snares at this point. The loops of the snares are spread across the path and look like normal vines which are scattered everywhere. There is a 25% chance per person of getting caught in a snare. (Check until all have gone past or all three snares have been set off.) When someone gets caught in a snare, he will be yanked out into the mire at one side of the path and immediately begin to sink. In addition, each victim will take 1d6 of damage from the snare itself. There are several Giant Leeches nearby that will attack anyone thrown into the mire. The seven Giant Leeches [AC: 9, HTK: 4, 8, 10, 12, 6, 7, 5 (2d8); 1 attack for 1-4 damage] will each drain 2 HTK in blood per round after the initial hit. There is only a 10% chance that the victim will be aware of the attack until 50% of HTK have been drained, or the victim gets out of the water.

TRAP 2: A ten foot deep pit has been dug here and covered with vines and other vegetation. The pit is ten feet wide (across the path) but only five feet long. In the bottom of the pit, the Gnoll Witchdoctor has placed three Poisonous Snakes [AC: 7, HTK: 11, 8, 9 (1d8+4); 1 attack for 1-2 HTK damage and poison]. They will attack anyone who falls in. Their poison, if not saved against, causes a loss of 4 points of Stamina per round. When less than 3 points is reached, the victim falls unconscious. When 0 or less points are reached, the victim is dead.

TRAP 3: Two snares have been set up here (similar to trap number one.) When these snares are triggered, the victim will be hoisted by one foot, ten feet into the air. Each victim must roll equal to or below his dexterity on a d20 in order to avoid dropping what he was holding at the time. In addition, each victim will take 1d6 of damage.

In a nearby tree are twelve Stirges [AC: 8, HTK: 6 each (1d8+1); 1 attack for 1-3 points damage] which have been charmed by the Gnoll Witchdoctor. (Thus allowing the Gnolls to set up the snares.) They will attack from behind as the party approaches the snares. Those caught in the snares will be the favorite targets of the Stirges. They will attack as 4d8 creatures and drain 1d4 HTK per round after the initial hit, with a maximum of 12 HTK drained per Stirge.

SWAMP ENCOUNTERS

As Myskip warned, the swamp is full of dangerous creatures. While the party is in the area of the swamp, roll every four hours for an encounter. On the main road, an encounter is indicated on a roll of 1 on a d8, and off the main road, an encounter is indicated on a roll of 1-2 on a

ENCOUNTER 2: A Giant Poisonous Snake [AC: 5, HTK: 29 (4d8+2); 1 attack for 1-3 plus poison] will drop from an over hanging tree on a random party member (surprise on a 1-4).

ENCOUNTER 3: Four Huge Spiders [AC: 6, HTK: 16, 12, 8, 14 (2d8+2); 1 attack for 1-6 plus poison] leap from surrounding vegetation into random party members. The Spiders will surprise on 1-5. The save vs. poison is at +1.

ENCOUNTER 4: A Catoblepas [AC: 7, HTK: 30 (6d8+2); 1 attack for 1-6 and stun] is quietly grazing in the bushes at the side of the path, with its head in the mire. Its tail, however, is stretched out across the path. As the party nears, the Catoblepas will lash out with its tail and begin to raise its head. There is a 25% chance each round that it will raise its head high enough to fix its gaze. If someone meets its gaze (only those foolish enough to be looking near its head), they will die with no saving throw. If no one meets the gaze of the Catoblepas, a random party member will have to save vs. death or die. If the party runs, the Catoblepas will give chase. Its gaze causes death. A strike from its tail has a 75% chance of stunning for 1d10 melee rounds (-5% per level above 1st).

THE GNOLL VILLAGES

There are two Gnoll villages in the Jovian swamp. Only the newer village is described in detail herein. For purposes of this adventure, the players should not need to go to the Gnolls' main village. In fact, they have been warned by Myskip not to take on all the Gnolls in the swamp. Should some fool-hardy group of adventurers end up in the old Gnoll village (marked "O"), it is up to the DM to roll up the inhabitants. Here are some basic guidelines in case this becomes necessary.

As stated in the background, the Gnolls are

d8. These odds for a random encounter double at night. The following is a list of encounters you may use. You may select them randomly or in any order you prefer:

ENCOUNTER 1: A Will'o'wisp [AC: -8, HTK: 48 (9d8); 1 attack for 2-16] will appear in the distance as several torches. It will attempt to lure the party off the path and into the bogs and quicksand.

experiencing an overpopulation problem. Therefore, there are about 450 Gnolls in the old village. The old village is about four times the size of the new one. The old village has walls quite similar to the new village, but they are higher and stronger. In addition to a Chieftain and his body guards, the following exceptional Gnolls will be found in the old village: 1 Shaman of 7th level, 2 of 5th level, 2 of 3rd level, and 1 of 2nd level. Also 1 Witchdoctor of 5th level, 2 of 3rd level, and 2 of 1st level. There are also about 50 adult male Gnolls of 3d8 HTK. The GM may want to further develop a description of this village for use in another adventure, perhaps as a sequel.

The new Gnoll village is on an island in the middle of the swamp (marked "G"). The layout of the village is shown on the second map. It is surrounded by a wooden stockade about fifteen feet high. At the base of the walls, wooden spikes are placed to fend off invaders. These spikes are slanted upward at a forty-five degree angle and are about four feet long. The only area along the walls that doesn't have these spikes is in front of the gates. The gates are also fifteen high, and bolted shut on the inside. Along the inside of the walls is a raised platform, about nine feet high, upon which the Gnoll watchmen stand. At any given time, there will be at least 10 Gnolls manning the walls.

Directly in front of the gate is a trap. A twenty foot deep pit has been dug, roofed over with wooden planks and covered with dirt. The pit covers an area of fifteen feet by fifteen feet. There are many two-foot long wooden spikes at the bottom of the pit. There is a lever just inside the gate that opens the pit. Anyone falling in the pit will take 4d6 of damage from the fall and the spikes.

Most of the buildings in the village are arranged around a central area. There are two wooden posts standing about three feet apart in the center of this area. Sacrificial victims are usually tied to these posts. The central area is used for meetings, religious ceremonies and celebrations (such as the wedding).

There are 45 adult male Gnolls in the village including the Chieftain, his 3 bodyguards, the 3 Shamans, and the Witchdoctor. There are also 10 adult females and 20 children. Therefore, the total population of this Gnoll settlement is 75. This may sound like a very small group of Gnolls, but you must remember that this is a very new settlement.

All buildings are mud brick structures with thatched roofs. Following is a description of each building. During the time of the ceremony, all Gnolls, except the wall guards, will be in the central area. The rest of the time, the Gnolls will be in the buildings, except for the ten on the walls. These ten Gnolls will be from buildings A and B. If the Gnolls spot the party, all the fighting males will join the guards on the platform.

A   General living quarters for unmarried males. Eight male Gnolls [AC: 5, HTK: 7, 9, 12, 9, 6, 13, 12, 5 (2d8)] occupy this hut and are armed with longswords and great bows. They have a treasure of 200 sp and 50 gp.

B   General living quarters for unmarried males. Nine male Gnolls [AC: 5, HTK: 7, 7, 9, 5, 6, 8, 11, 7, 14 (2d8)] occupy this hut and are armed with longswords and halberds. They have a treasure of 210 sp, 73 gp, and 2 gems worth 10 gp and 25 gp.

C   General living quarters for two married couples. They have a treasure of 235 sp, 100 gp, and 3 gems (worth 25 gp, 25 gp, 50 gp).
    2 male Gnolls [AC: 5, HTK: 13, 12 (2d8); armed with longswords and great bows]
    2 female Gnolls [AC: 7, HTK: 9, 7 (2d8); unarmed]
    3 young Gnolls [AC: 8, HTK: 5, 4, 6 (1d8); unarmed]

D   Chieftain's living quarters. The Chieftain (and soon his bride) occupy this hut. The Chieftain's bodyguards also live here. (They will move out after the wedding.) This is where Yolanda [Magic User, Skill: 4, AC: 10, HTK: 12] is being kept. Note that Yolanda has no spells left, and since she has no books, she won't be able to gain any. The Chief has the following treasure: 1,000 sp, 800 gp, and 10 gems (worth 100 gp, 100 gp, 50 gp, 25 gp, 25 gp, 25 gp, 25 gp, 10 gp, 10 gp, 10 gp).
    Chieftain [AC: 3 (+2 armor), HTK: 32 (5d8); armed with a +2 two-handed sword]
    3 Gnoll bodyguards [AC: 4 (shields), HTK: 29, 20, 17 (4d8); armed with longswords and spears]

E   General living quarters for unmarried males. Six male Gnolls [AC: 4 (shields), HTK: 8, 10, 9, 12, 8, 9 (2d8)] occupy this hut and are armed with longswords and spears. They have a treasure of 300 sp, 45 gp, and 2 gems (worth 30 gp and 20 gp)

F   General living quarters. Two married couples occupy

Gnoll village

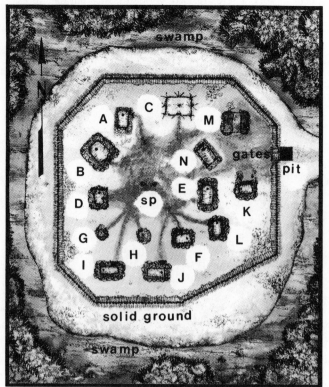

scale: **20 ft.** **sp sacrifice posts**

(Shaman 1): Cure Light Wounds (2), Hold Person;
(Shaman 2): Cure Light Wounds, Light, Chant]
2 female Gnolls [AC: 7, HTK: 9, 10 (2d8); unarmed]
4 young Gnolls [AC: 8, HTK: 6, 7, 9, 5 (1d8); unarmed]

J General living quarters for unmarried males. Eight male Gnolls [AC: 5, HTK: 7, 7, 9, 6, 11, 10, 8, 9 (2d8), armed with longswords and spears] occupy this hut. They have a treasure of 200 sp, 110 gp, and 1 gem (worth 25 gp).

K Supply Hut/Smithy. Various supplies are kept here, including weapons, armor, building materials, etc. There is also a supply of raw iron and materials for the

this hut. They have a treasure of 300 sp, 120 gp, and 4 gems (worth 25 gp, 25 gp, 10 gp, 10 gp).
2 male Gnolls [AC: 4 (shields), HTK: 10, 13 (3d8); armed with longswords and spears]
2 female Gnolls [AC: 7, HTK: 9, 8 (2d8); unarmed]
6 young Gnolls [AC: 8, HTK: 5, 6, 4, 3, 2, 7 (1d8); unarmed]

G Tribal Shaman's living quarters. The Tribal Shaman, his wife, and their children live here. They have a treasure of 750 sp, 500 gp, 5 gems (worth 75 gp, 50 gp, 50 gp, 25 gp, 10 gp), and 2 Potions of Healing.
Tribal Shaman [AC: 5, HTK: 30 (5d8); armed with a Staff of Withering. Spells: Cure Light Wounds (2), Light, Hold Person (2), Silence, Prayer]
Female Gnoll [AC: 7, HTK: 5 (2d8); unarmed]
2 young Gnolls [AC: 8, HTK: 4, 3 (1d8); unarmed]

H Witchdoctor's living quarters. The Tribal Witchdoctor lives here with his wife and 3 children.
Tribal Witchdoctor [AC: 6, HTK: 24 (3d8); armed with longsword; Spells: Charm Person, Magic Missile, Web]
Female Gnoll [AC: 7, HTK: 10 (2d8); unarmed]
3 young Gnolls [AC: 8, HTK: 5, 6, 7 (1d8); unarmed]

I Shamans' living quarters. Two other Shamans and their wives live here. Each Shaman has two children. They have a treasure of 500 sp, 150 gp, and 4 gems (worth 100 gp, 50 gp, 10 gp, 10 gp).
2 Gnoll Shamans [AC: 5, HTK: 17, 20 (3d8); Spells

smithy which is located outside of the building, by the doorway.

L   General living quarters for two married couples live here with their children.
    2 male Gnolls [AC: 5, HTK: 12, 13 (2d8); armed with longswords and great bows]
    2 female Gnolls [AC: 7, HTK: 5, 7 (2d8); unarmed]
    2 young Gnolls [AC: 8, HTK: 5, 6 (1d8)]

M   This is not so much a building as a pen for livestock. It is divided into sections for pigs and goats.

N   This is also not actually a building, but a temporary tent set up for the 15 visiting male Gnolls. (see below)

There are already an additional 15 adult males visiting the village from their southern home. On the day the ceremony is to take place, the old chieftain, his daughter, 5 additional adult females, and 19 additional adult male Gnoll guards will be present. Here is a list of all these additional Gnolls:
15 male Gnolls [AC: 5, HTK: (armed with two handed swords) 11, 5, 7, 7, 9, 8, 15, 7, 14 (armed with battleaxes and halberds) 10, 8, 9, 10, 9 (2d8)].

Arriving on the wedding day:
    10 male Gnolls [AC: 4, HTK: 6, 9, 14, 13, 11, 11, 5, 6, 10, 8 (2d8), armed with battleaxes and spears]
    5 male Gnolls [AC: 5, HTK: 15, 14, 11, 6, 14 (2d8), armed with longswords and great bows]
    5 female Gnolls [AC: 7, HTK: 7, 6, 12, 7, 12 (2d8)]
    Old Chieftain [AC: 4, HTK: 34 (5d8), armed with +3 battleaxe]
    Old Chieftain's guards [AC: 4, HTK: 18, 21, 22, 14 (4d8), armed with battleaxes]
    Old Chieftain's daughter [AC: 7, HTK: 14 (2d8)]

THE WEDDING

On the night of the wedding, most of the Gnolls will be in the central area of the village to attend the ceremony. There will, however, be 20 Gnolls manning the walls at this time. Most of the village will be in a state of frenzied chaos until it gets close to midnight. At that time, the Gnolls not on watch duty will gather near the sacrifice posts. The new Chieftain and his bride will stand before the posts, and the Tribal Shaman will begin a wild dance around them. The two assistant Shamans will then bring Yolanda out of the Chieftain's hut, and tie her to the posts. The Tribal Shaman will then hand both the bride and the groom long iron daggers. At this point, they begin a dance around the posts, ending with the groom in front of the victim and the bride behind her. The crowd will become completely silent as they raise their daggers. Simultaneously, they will plunge their daggers into the victim. At this point, they are married and the feast begins.

Hopefully, the rescue party will arrive before this all takes place, but it is described here in case they attive just in time (or just too late). During the latter parts of the ceremony, it is likely that the guards on the walls will be busy trying to see the ceremony from their posts, and not watching too carefully.

If an attack interrupts the wedding ceremony, the Gnolls will attempt to keep Yolanda alive. If the battle looks lost, then the Tribal Shaman will attempt to kill her.

Remember, Yolanda must be returned safely to Myskip! If she is killed as part of the wedding ceremony, she will not be able to be raised because her soul will have been taken by Zyrmgnollven! Once the party gets Yolanda out of the village, they must still return to Jovian Delta. A random encounter at this point might be just enough to finish off a battle-weary party! If they make it all the way back to Jovian Delta, the party will be hailed as heros. Myskip will, of course, pay the promised reward and swear his undying gratitude to each member of the party.

KOBOLDS

by Alan Nudelman

KOBOLD PRELUDE

In every universe, there are the meek, the mild, the down-trodden. In every world, there are the small and the weak. In every campaign, there are the monsters simply thrown in for comic relief.

For centuries, Kobolds have played these roles. They have been abused, scorned, and mocked. They were the target of pointed wit and ugly sarcasm, the one monster everyone could laugh at without fear of reprisal. Indeed, Kobolds got no respect.

But times are ready to change. The Kobold nation is ready to assume its place in the gallery of evil creatures. Huge tribes have armed and built themselves into fierce fighting units. They have trained until the countryside echoed with their battle cries. Orcs, Hobgoblins, Trolls, and Gnolls will quiver with fear as the mighty Kobold armies advance. Kobolds are prepared to wreak havoc among the good and overcome the cities of humans, dwarves, and elves. They are poised to plunder, loot, and steal throughout the land. They will attack, they will conquer, they will assume their destinies as masters of the known universe.

Then again, maybe not . . .

KOBOLD VITAL STATISTICS

Kobolds are small creatures descended from reptiles. They grow to three and a half feet tall and have a slightly scaly hide, rudimentary claws, and large teeth. Kobolds have excellent night vision and infravision, but cannot function well in open sunlight. Singly, they are rather timid and cowardly, but in large groups, they gain courage and usually attack opponents on sight. They are very tribe-oriented and as wandering monsters will be encountered in groups of five to fifty adult males.

A tribe of Kobolds will contain 20d20 mature males. There will be three times as many females and six times as many hatchlings as mature males. There will also be one egg for every two adult males. Thus, the total number of Kobolds in a tribe may number in the thousands.

Kobolds have 1d4 HTK each and have AC: 7. The leader of a tribe will always have 4 HTK. For every hundred adult males, there will be an officer with 3 or 4 HTK. With every group of ten, there will be a sargeant with 3 or 4 HTK.

Kobold Witchdoctors and Shamans will only be found in the lair. There will be one Witchdoctor for every hundred adult males. These are under the direct control of the leader. Shamans will be twice as numerous as Witchdoctors. One quarter of the Shamans serve Farhet and are under the command of the leader, while the remainder will be Shamans of Morhet under the matriarchal leader (see the section on Kobold Gods).

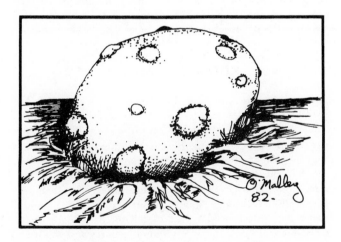

Like reptiles, Kobolds are hatched from eggs. A Kobold female can lay an egg every two years. The incubation period lasts three months. After another three months, hatchlings are able to fend for themselves outside the nest. During these first three months, the females tend the young and train them in the fundamentals of Kobold life.

Most Kobolds survive while in the nest, but then their mortality rate rises dramatically. Only one in twenty survive to reach physical and sexual maturity after ten years. Kobolds can live up to 125 years, although their average life expectancy is only four years.

KOBOLD SOCIETY STRUCTURE

The chain of command in Kobold society is based completely on age. The oldest Kobolds are the leaders. They direct battle, get first pick of the women and inhabit the choicest quarters. The youngest Kobolds, the hatchlings, are always at the front of battle. They are so numerous that the casualties suffered in combat are quickly replaced by new hatchlings. Youngsters surviving their first battle are placed further away from combat and get to move into more comfortable quarters. Further survival means more benefits.

Until their tenth year of life, hatchlings also serve as the menial servants for the Kobold tribe. They clean the quarters, herd the Gelatinous Cubes that keep the common areas clean, cook and serve food, empty chamber pots, and obey the orders of the older Kobolds. Parties of hatchlings go on hunting expeditions under the direction of young officers, learning the same techniques that will later be used in battle. During this time, the desire to survive to an older age becomes very acute.

The younger Kobolds occasionally have fun. They enjoy tormenting small animals, playing tricks on younger hatchlings and generally causing trouble, while staying out of the way of their elders. They are especially fond of the rather dangerous adventure of stealing the young of Giant Weasels, Otters, or Boars. These wild animals are tamed by the females in the Kobold nest to serve as guards when they reach full size. The Kobold casualties from these expeditions are seldom missed.

Young female hatchlings are indistinguishable from their male counterparts both in appearance and treatment received. They train with the males, they fight alongside the males, and are treated just as badly as the male Kobolds. Once they reach maturity, the females are placed in a position of honor and respect. They occupy the finest rooms, get the best food, and are treated like the exceptional creatures that they are. Like males, the leadership structure for females is based on age. Kobold females have little respect for each other and the older females readily mete out punishment. In this, they are no different than the older males.

While the older females are living in the comparitive lap of luxury, the older males are undergoing a continuation of the brutal treatment they survived in their younger years. Their training goes on in small groups with an officer conducting the necessay drills and lessons. The young adults often take groups of hatchlings out on hunting expeditions. in doing this, the adults gain experience in leadership and food gathering for the Kobold tribe. In general, the treatment of an older Kobold is a shade less intimidating then the earlier brutalities, since an older Kobold has proven his ability to survive.

Only the lawful nature of Kobolds permits this rather brutal system of hierarchy to persevere. The leader of a group possesses absolute authority. Any disobedience is handled in the training cadre, with the evil nature of Kobold providing effective punishment. Torture is popular and various forms of mental abuse are also encouraged.

Battle training starts as soon as the hatchling leaves the nest and continues until maturity. Lessons include stalking, slinking, hiding, and other useful skills. Hiding is one of the

groups. However, their small size encouraged larger creatures to molest and belittle them, eventually forcing tribes to retreat from contact with their harrassers.

Orcs and Gnomes were the last two races to maintain contact with Kobolds. Forest Kobolds were allied with Orcs until the chaotic nature of the hideous snout-faced creatures became too repugnant to bear. The alliance broke off when an Orcish army betrayed several groups of Kobold scouting parties during a battle, revealing their locations when the Orcs were captured.

The alliance with the Gnomes lasted several centuries longer. Gnomes, adept at excavating and mining, provided Kobolds with comfortable homes. After exhausting veins of ore, Gnomes would smooth the floors and walls and turn over the finished lair to Kobold tribes. Kobolds kept Gnomes supplied with forest products, fresh meat, and other valuable commodities.

Racial strife was causing relations to be strained when disaster struck. An underground Kobold lair, tunneled out and turned over after the Gnomes had finished mining, turned out to be attached to the den of a sleeping Red Dragon. The Dragon, awakening after several decades, crawled out from this unexplored portion of the complex into the nest of the Kobold tribe. Only a few Kobolds survived the series of breaths to tell the story to the rest of the world. The Gnomes, feeling responsible for the disaster, rushed to the scene, subdued the Dragon, and began cleaning up. The Orcs, hated foes of Kobolds and Gnomes, spread a rumor that the Gnomes were eating roasted Kobold eggs. Ready to believe the worst, the suspicious Kobolds sent a huge raiding party into the scorched lair, slaughtered dozens of Gnomes, and fled into the night. Since that time, Kobolds have distrusted all other races and sworn undying hatred towards Gnomes.

KOBOLD HABITATS

Kobolds are not adept builders or excavators. In the forest, they live in crudely constructed wood or grass huts. They prefer to live in caverns and often overrun complexes excavated by other races. Because of their sensitive eyes, they are never found in the open during the daytime.

Kobold dwellings are kept surprisingly clean. It is the duty of the hatchlings to clean the lair. This is accomplished through much manual labor, but is made easier by the astonishing fact that Kobolds actually keep Gelatinous Cubes as organic vacuum cleaners and will herd them with torches from hall to hall, scouring the common areas of an underground complex.

At the very center of a dwelling, in the most protected area, will be found the mature females, young hatchlings, and the eggs. This will be one of the larger caverns, since the females outnumber males by three to one. The nest area will be very well guarded and repeatedly, although clumsily, trapped. There will always be sufficient escape routes for the occupants of the nest.

Going outward from the maternity ward are rooms for the chiefs, the officers, and so on down until the young hatchlings are found inhabiting the numerous outside rooms at the edge of the lair. There will be rooms for cooking and communal dining. These are accessible to outside entrances for easy delivery of food gathered and

most important lessons since the ambush is one of the most successful tactics employed. Battle training is mostly psychological, since the small size of a Kobold precludes effective utilization of the champion concept. Kobolds are taught to quietly whip themselves into a battle fury, erupting into melee with blood-curdling screams and much gnashing of teeth. Older Kobolds learn archery. No battlefield tactics are taught, since Kobolds are never involved in open field combat.

KOBOLD RELATIONSHIPS

Kobolds have a pathological distrust of all other sentient races. They will always attack or flee from an encounter, never negotiating or surrendering. Treaties will never be formed with another race, although agreements between tribes of Kobolds are common.

Many years ago, Kobolds were more social than they are now. They prospered as weavers, farmers, and hunters, with their lawful nature allowing efficient cooperation in

captured by foraging parties. Areas are set aside for the construction of primitive weapons and armor. Two temple areas will be near the center of the lair. Rooms for Witchdoctors to study and practice are located near the leader's quarters.

Animals reared in the Kobold tribe are scattered throughout the lair and often accompany hunting parties. These creatures are trained by the elder females to guard the nest and to serve as sentries. Weasels and Boars will be found with a tribe 75% of the time while Wildcats and Otters will be found less commonly (only 25% of the time).

KOBOLD PROTECTIVE COLORING

Kobolds are a dark brown to black in color. In an underground setting, they blend well with stone walls and tend to be virtually indistinguishable in normal darkness. A single Kobold has a 90% chance of remaining unnoticed if immobile. (This is usually the state of a single Kobold, since they quickly tend to become rooted to the ground in fear.)

In deep woods, the Kobold's color becomes a dark to light blue hue due to the light coming through the underbrush. The numerous hiding places in a forest makes this terrain ideal for the Kobolds' ambushing tactics.

KOBOLD TRAPS

Kobolds protect their lairs with crude but numerous traps. These are set so that the smaller Kobolds can pass by unharmed while their heavy and tall foes detonate the traps. Snares are set to sweep by at about four feet high. Trip wires are set at a foot and a half, high enough for

Kobolds to see and duck under, but low enough to be easy to miss in a dark dungeon. Pits dug by Kobolds are concealed by woven mats that would support a number of Kobolds while collapsing under the weight of a man-size being. These traps are especially common along routes of escape planned by the Kobold officers.

Traps in a lair are usually marked about a foot off the ground. This is less for the benefit of other Kobolds than it is to insure the traps remain set. These markings blend into the wall and normally would only be noticed by Kobolds who are trained to look for them. Non-Kobolds will notice 10% of the time there is something marked on a wall. Even when found, markings will be misinterpreted 25% of the time, as each Kobold tribe has its own peculiar set of symbols.

A trap set by a Kobold will deliver 1-3d6 of damage. Poison is never used, although spikes are common. Traps are typically set near ambush sites, enabling an extra element of surprise while a trap is avoided or disarmed. The nest of a tribe will be extensively trapped as well as heavily guarded.

KOBOLD MAGIC

There will be one Kobold Witchdoctor for every hundred adult males in a tribe. These Kobolds are chosen by the leader of a tribe after they reach maturity. The 25% of Kobolds surviving the twenty years of training will be able to use first and second level spells at up to fourth level of ability. Witchdoctors are under the direct control of the Kobold leader.

Magic items are highly prized by the Kobold tribes. Since only the most skilled of the Kobold Witchdoctors are able to attempt the manufacture of items, Kobold magic items are extremely rare. Any normal magic item invariably has been stolen.

MORHET'S RING is one of these highly prized items. They are so rare that only the male leader of the tribe will have them. The Ring is able to heal up to 36 HTK of damage a day as the damage is incurred. Any damage will instantly be averted for the wearer of this Ring. The Ring also allows the user to teleport without error once per day at eighth level of ability. The item recharges at dawn. The ring is cursed so that each point of damage cured will age the wearer by one month. Only 25% of Kobold tribes will have this item, with 5% of these having a second Ring. If two Rings are possessed, the male leader will have both of them.

THE HORN OF FARHET is another Kobold magic item. When blown, anyone within one hundred feet of the Horn will assume the morale of a Kobold (normal saving throw versus magic applies). They will run away if outnumbered, start taking morale checks after the third round of melee, and so on. (See section of Kobold attack and melee.) The effect of the Horn wears off after one turn or after the affected party flees for 1d6 rounds. 50% of Kobold tribes will have this item.

THE RING OF WEIGHT was one of the items which the Gnomes taught the Kobolds how to make. When worn, the mass of the wearer will increase to that of a large horse, with a corresponding strength increase for movement only. Thus an opponent, expecting a normal Kobold, will be caught off balance when one weighing as much as a horse charges into battle. Damage from a charge is 2d6, while falling on an opponent will cause 3d6 of damage. These Rings are the most common of Kobold magical items, with one in a hundred Kobolds having them.

No known Kobold artifacts exists, although they may use and do envy artifacts used by other dark folk.

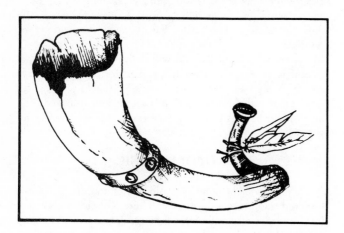

KOBOLD GODS

Kobolds worship only two gods: Farhet, the god of bravery and courage in battle; and Morhet, the goddess of

safety in retreat. These gods are never worshipped at the same time.

Farhet, the greater of the two, is worshipped only by Kobold warriors in time of approaching and unavoidable battle. The Shamans of Farhet are exclusively male and are taken randomly from Kobolds reaching maturity. Their training includes learning the necessary ceremonies and practicing the few spells they are able to cast. Battle training is also provided, although at a slightly lower fatality level than non-clerical battle training.

Sacrifices of food and small animals accompany much loud cheering in a ceremony dedicated to Farhet. His Shamans wear orange robes and are adept at casting up to second level spells at third level of ability. The symbol of the god is a large Kobold swinging a sword larger than himself.

There is a 1% chance that Farhet will appear and assist Kobolds in battle if melee continues for more than five rounds. He appears as a 6 foot tall, golden-skinned Kobold who weighs about 300 pounds. He is a 15th level fighter and has no magical abilities. Farhet has AC: -6 and 157 HTK. The sight of Farhet gives Kobolds normal morale and will invoke fear in any other race in sight.

The goddess Morhet is worshipped by female Kobolds and also male Kobolds not expecting battle. She protects the Kobolds as they flee or hide from danger. Not surprisingly, the Shamans of Morhet are exclusively female, with the eldest Shaman holding the most power. Usually the eldest Shaman of Morhet will also rule the tribe, although the male Kobolds never openly acknowledge her leadership. While many simple decisions will be made by the male leader, the female will always be consulted and inevitably deferred to on major issures. Ceremonies for Morhet consist of releasing small animals into the darkness, singing, and burning of incense.

Morhet appears as a darkly robed figure around four feet high. She can not be hit from the rear by any weapon or magical spell. She has perfect teleportation ability and can heal any wound. She can appear in battle when summoned if the safety of a retreating tribe is threatened (1% chance) or the nest is attacked (5% chance). Morhet has AC: -4 from the front, 120 HTK, and 85% magic resistance. She fights, when necessary, as a 5th level fighter, but also casts clerical spells and protective magic spells as a 17th level cleric or mage. She does not compete with Farhet, but instead assists when necessary and will come to his aid when he is in mortal (or divine) danger.

KOBOLD ATTACK AND MELEE

Kobolds will not attack unless they expect to be able to overwhelm their foes in less than four melee rounds. Usually this means Kobolds outnumber their opponents by more than three to one or that they are bigger than their opponents. They will always attack Gnomes on sight.

Typically, front line Kobolds are unarmed (1-4 damage with bite) or equipped with short swords (equivalent to daggers for damage, 1d4/1d3) or axes (1d4). Since these are the youngest of the tribe (older ones learn to stay to the rear), they attack with incredible zeal and almost unbelievable stupidity. Kobold archers fire their dart-like arrows (1d3/1d2) without regard for the safety of their companions in melee; the larger opponents are more likely to be hit, but any arrows falling short inevitably hit a Kobold. Typical Kobold battle cries consist of pleas to Farhet for strength and insults about the foes, usually comparing them to Gnomes.

In taking morale checks, any negative adjustments should be take at triple normal penalty; in any case, Kobolds start thinking of running away if the opponents are not overwhelmed by the end of the third melee round.

KOBOLD AMBUSH

Kobolds usually attack from ambush. Their small size makes hiding places easy to find, even in relatively sparse surroundings. Kobolds have been known to hide behind rocks, inside armor, chests, and furniture, and even to cling to spider webs when setting ambushes. Normally, the excellent skill of these small creatures in hiding and moving silently would give them a better chance to surprise opponents. However, since so many Kobolds are usually involved in an attack, they have only a two in six chance of surprise.

KOBOLD RETREAT

After the ambush, the most important Kobold fighting tactic is retreat. Almost any unexpected or unfamiliar tactic will cause Kobolds to flee in utter panic. Even the simplest illusions will scare enough of the Kobolds to convince the others of impending mortal danger. Due to the number of Kobolds involved in a melee, retreat will allow at least 90% of the survivors to escape, since a retreat will be in all directions. Typically (75%), weapons will be dropped, further complicating pursuit.

If Kobolds are cornered, they will usually (90%) surrender. Questioning is usually fruitless, since captured Kobolds are panicked into incomprehensibility. However, if the main nest room of a Kobold tribe is attacked, the guards will defend fearlessly until the eggs are safely removed through one of the many escape routes planned.

THE TOWER

INTRODUCTION

You arrived in the town of Aspregull, located in the foothills of the Great White Mountains, ten days ago. Bone tired and weary from your long journey, you procured lodging at the Green Dragon Inn, a small, comfortable hostelry. Now you are rested, bored, and broke. Unless you can find a way to earn some money soon, you will be evicted.

That evening, while drinking at the bar, an urchin tugs at your arm. "Mister," he wails, "Mister, come with me. Come with me!" You smile, pluck his hand from your arm, push him toward the door, and continue drinking your ale. You feel a hesitant tug at your cloak, and a timid voice says, "Mister, please. He told me to bring you."

You perk up. "What's this? You were sent here?"

"Yes, mister. If you don't come, I won't get no gold .. .. Please come!"

You are definitely interested now. Someone rich enough to hand out gold to an urchin might prove to be a generous employer. You follow the filthy guttersnipe to an armory in the better part of town. The child leads you to the front door, and steps through. In the darkness, you see a Dwarf forging a sword. He motions you to a side door and returns to work. Entering the side room, you find a number of people already waiting there; they are all wearing armor and carrying weapons.

A few minutes later, the Dwarf enters the room and greets you. He tosses the youngster a gold piece, who smiles as he scurries from the room. The Dwarf begins to speak:

"Thank you for answering my summons. I, Balathor, am in need of your assistance and you, I gather from your prompt arrival, are in need of gold." He smiles briefly, noting your flush of discomfort. "Some of you may know that the Dwarven stronghold of Hawkhelm is not far from here.

"One hundred years ago, our people left to take part in a northern war with the forces of goblinkind. The entrances to the underground areas were sealed against entry and I was left in charge of a small contingent to maintain the

Keep and guard against intruders. Although we longed to go with our friends, we accepted our assignment. For fifty-three years all went well, until a great earthquake destroyed three of the Keep's towers and all of the walls. The fourth tower of the Keep collapsed partially, but the lower floors held firm, saving my life. My friends were not as lucky; all were killed.

"I spent the next fifteen years trying to find an entryway into the underground sections of the city, but to no avail. All entrances were blocked with earth and rubble. I tried, but was unable to unearth an entrance alone. Finally, I gave up and sealed the remains of the tower. Wishing to remain in the area, I moved to Aspregull, took up my old profession and waited for my kinsmen to return. On the hundredth anniversary of the departure of my people, I took a day's vacation and visited my old home.

"Nearing the stronghold, I was shocked to discover Kobolds in the forests. All signs seemed to indicate that a Kobold tribe was entrenched in the underground complex I once called home. Watching throughout the night, I confirmed my suspicions; many Kobolds entered and exited the tower; somehow, they had uncovered an entrance that I had failed to find. I must now commission others to remove the Kobold menace from my home. I require that you find a way into the underground complex and remove the Kobolds. It is not likely that the Kobolds will have retained much of the dwarven wealth that was sealed below. Any valuables that you discover, except for artifacts belonging to my people, may be kept by your party. I am willing to pledge my funds against these dwarven items, to insure a hefty profit for your party."

He stops, looks carefully at each of you and asks, "What say you — will you take this mission?"

DM ONLY: Balathor will guarantee the party a minimum sum of 1,000 gp each. He will provide the party with a map that will direct them to the Keep, but will not go with the party.

Although he will not offer to do so, Balathor is willing to equip the party out of the guarantee he is offering. Any armor bought from him will be of the best quality and will be sold at no markup. He has one +1 sword he is willing to let the party use. He can also vouch for the group at other shops in town, assuring them of reasonable prices for once.

Balathor knows quite a bit about Kobolds, but he assumes the party knows just as much. He will answer any questions about the dungeon layout and Kobolds, but knows nothing about the current status of the complex. He will suggest the party check the northeast corner of the first and third levels for safe camping, in that the dwarven temple is protected by a spell to ward off evil. He also warns the party not to disturb the northeast corner of the tower's basement, where he says the dwarven founders of the Keep are entombed.

The townspeople of Aspregull know Balathor and will speak well of him and his work. They also know of the tower, but will warn of great peril for any who enter it. A rumor, started many years ago by the dwarven community to keep the tower and cavern complex isolated, has, over the years, had the desired effect, for now all the mothers of Aspregull warn that only dwarves can enter the tower and live. The rumors are false.

There are 120 adult male Kobolds in the complex. Many of the leaders are in the lowest level in the choicest rooms. A few occupy the trade rooms on the second level. Most of the first floor and the second floor trade rooms are occupied by 720 unarmed hatchlings. The large meeting room in the bottom level has 300 adult females, 60 newly hatched Kobolds and 60 eggs. It is heavily guarded, repeatedly trapped and has 7 escape routes in various places.

Unless otherwise noted, all Kobolds have 1d4 HTK and are AC: 7. They do 1d4 HTK of damage with a bite, 1d6 if armed with a hand-held weapon and 1d3 with arrows. When attacking, they will initially swarm over their opponents, yelling, screaming, cursing, and comparing their opponents to Gnomes. If the party is not overwhelmed within 3 melee rounds, give the Kobolds a morale check at 50%. If they make their morale roll (01-50), continue rolling in successive rounds at -5% per round. If they fail, they will run away in all directions, possibly trampling other Kobolds in their way. (There is a 10% chance they will surrender if cornered, otherwise, they will engage with intent to escape.) In any case, fleeing Kobolds will warn others that danger is near, thus giving them a chance to set an ambush.

Adjustments to Kobold morale are as follows:

-15%	25% of party eliminated or slain
-30%	leader unconscious (he's in the rear)
-45%	50%+ of party eliminated or slain
-90%	leader killed (he's in the rear)
-30%	taking casualties without inflicting any

KOBOLD WILDERNESS

The tower and underground complex are southwest of Aspregull, near the base of the Great White Mountains. Near the tower, a stream runs into the forest. The Kobold tribe is constantly hunting in the forest in groups of ten to one hundred (10d10). If a random encounter is indicated, roll 1d8 first, and on a roll of one have the encounter be Kobolds. Since the forest is quite thick, do not penalize the Kobolds for daytime exposure.

As is usual with Kobolds, there are several escape tunnels nearby. However, these are heavily camouflaged and not used, except in emergencies. Should the party look for the tunnels, there is only a 2% chance that they will find one. The tunnel will too small for any but gnomes or halflings to use (if entered, the tunnel will lead them to the nest (level 3 room 9) where all of the guards will immediately attack without regard to morale).

THE DWARVEN TOWER

The tower supports the only remaining remnants of the walls that surround the Castle Keep. Kobolds will be patrolling the tower in two groups of 2d4. Their function is to alert the Kobold tribe below. Roll 1d6 every 2 rounds. On a one, the party will encounter a group of Kobolds. If any Kobolds get away, the lower levels will be on alert for the next sixty minutes.

1. This is the basement of the tower. A spiral staircase leads up in the southwest corner. A trap door leads

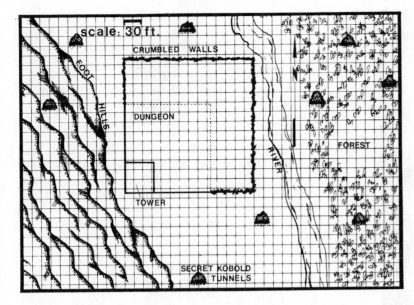

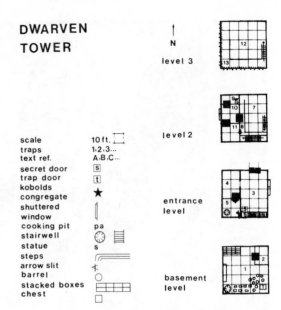

down from the southeast corner. Boxes containing food and waterskins are stacked in the northwast corner. Barrels full of wine and water are in the southeast corner in front of the trap door. Seven empty chests are along the south wall. (One has a false bottom with 3 gems worth 50 gp each.) A number of spears, bows and arrows, swords, and daggers are scattered along the north wall. An empty cabinet is on the west wall.

If alerted, there will be 5d10 Kobolds from the lower level defending the entrance to the lair. These Kobolds will all fight for a minimum of three melee rounds, One fifth of them will be behind the boxes in the northwest. Two fifths will be crouched behind the kegs armed with bows and arrows. One fifth will be hiding inside the empty chests. One fifth will be on the stairs leading up ready to charge. If not alerted by a battle outside, there will be 3-12 Kobolds milling about the room.

Several stairs on the spiral staircase have been replaced with woven straw mats painted black to resemble metal steps. If a party member falls or as the first adventurer is reaching the bottom, the Kobolds will attack. Damage from the fall is 2d4; save vs. death for half damage. The Kobolds in the chests are waiting for the party to move into the room and present their backs.

2   Seven dwarven patriarchs are buried here. There is a wizard-locked door on the west wall. A warning in common, dwarven, elven, orcish, gnomish, good, neutral, and evil states anyone who disturbs this tomb will die a horrible death. (A Permanent Symbol of Death is on the east wall; all who enter will die. The symbol cannot be dispelled or neutralized.) The bodies interred are wearing mithril armor, have +3 returning dwarven war hammers by their sides, and have pouches containing 3,000 gp on their belts. Thus, they have lain in state for 2,000 years.

3   Foyer and cloak room. Large double doors lead in; they are securely barred on the inside. There is a window with sturdy shutters on the east wall. A secret door in the south wall leads to the landing of a stairway.

4   Empty room. The floor is covered with woven grass mats.

5   A sunken room. The floor appears to be covered with woven mats, but is actually 5' lower than Room 4 and the stairway landing 6. These mats are propped up in the middle and are strong enough to support Kobolds. When walked on by larger creatures, they will collapse and cause victims to suffer 1d4 HTK of damage, save vs. death for half damage. Steps under the mats lead up to the doors in the north and east walls. The spiral staircase has been built up five feet to match the level of the mats. The top five feet of the staircase is crudely constructed of wood, while below the mats, it is made of finely wrought metal. Every tenth stairstep has been removed and replaced with a false step made of woven straw and pointed black. These steps are not readily apparent without close inspection. When one of the false steps are stepped on, they will collapse for 1d4 HTK of damage with a save vs. death for half damage.

Three Kobolds are below the mats on watch. They will not fight, but will run down the spiral staircase to warn the others.

6   Landing for staircase leading up to level 2.

7   Dining room covered with thick layer of dust. One path has been walked repeatedly; it leads from the staircase in the southeast corner to the entrance in the northwest corner. Several dust-covered tables are stacked in the southwest corner.

8   5' wide corridor. The door in the southeast leads to the stairway down.

9   Empty room. Hidden trap door in southeast corner opens up to reveal a small chest with 300 gp.

gather in a given room with an asterisk (*) and wait for the attackers to spring the trap nearby. When the trap is encountered, Kobolds will attack from the room. They have practiced this maneuver constantly and, thus, if a party passes one of these rooms, there is a 50% chance the Kobolds will spring out and attack from behind. (The rooms were once apartments for dwarves.)

2   These rooms contain 6-36 (6d6) Kobolds and 1d3 Boars (50%) or 1d4 Weasels (40%) each. A Kobold leader with 4 HTK will be directing the attacks of the other Kobolds and the trained animals. If forced into battle, the leader will remain to the rear with at least one of the animals for protection. (The rooms were once apartments for dwarves.)

3   A gaming room. There are six kegs of beer in the southeast corner. Ropes and nets are stretched across the ceiling for a decorative effect. Four small chests lie in the northest corner. These are filled with gaming equipment. (One of the chests has a false bottom in which will be found seven gems worth 100 gp each.) Two dart boards are spiked to the south wall and ten mugs hang on pegs on the east wall. Above the pegs is the following inscription:

3 3 5 4 4 3 5 . . .

(Since the first seven numbers are the number of letters in the numbers from one to seven, the next three numbers would be five, four, and three. Pushing pegs five, four, and three in order will cause 20 gp to drop from a hole in the ceiling. The Kobolds have never figured this out.)

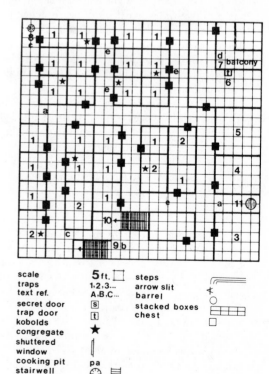

10   This room contains 1d12 Kobold guards, armed with bows and arrows, who are supposed to be watching for intruders. The room is sparsely furnished with stools and a few small mats.

11   10 empty casks are stacked in the southwest corner of this otherwise empty room.

12   Training area. Now empty.

13   Defensive area with arrow slits on south and west walls. It is not currently occupied. A set of stairs in the east end leads down to level 2.

THE UNDERGROUND LEVELS
FIRST LEVEL ROOMS

1   These rooms contain five to twenty (5d4) Kobolds each. They are unarmed but do 1d4 HTK damage with bites when they hit. If Kobolds, fleeing from the tower, sound the alarm on this level, the hatchlings will

5d8 Kobolds will be casually rolling dice, throwing darts, etc, if the alarm is not given. If the Kobolds are warned, this will be an ambush site, with eight Kobolds crouching behind kegs, two Kobolds inside each chest, and fifteen more hanging from the ropes and nets near in the ceiling. Half will be armed with short swords, the others will be unarmed.

4 Ceramics room. Crude pottery is made here for the Kobold tribe. A kiln in the northeast corner sits under an air vent smoke hole which leads up to the surface. A latched window in the north part of the west wall can be opened from the inside and can serve as a means of escape for the Kobolds in the room. 1d6+4 Kobolds are in this room, sleeping during the day and working during the night. They are unarmed but will throw pots for 1d3 HTK damage before engaging with bites. Six large pots are in the southeast corner of the room; 1-3 Kobolds will be hiding in them.

5 Metal working shop. Kobolds do not know how to smelt ore, but can mend cracks in knives, swords, and other metal untensils. 1d4+4 Kobolds will be in this room, sleeping during the day and working during the night. They are armed with spears and swords.

6 Dwarven temple meeting area. The dwarven temple extends up to this level from the bottom of the complex (see level 3, room 5 for a description of the temple area). It is guarded by a permanent Protection spell that kills any evil being entering the area. (Evil creatures with more than 6d8 HTK are entitled to a saving throw.) The door has Kobold inscriptions warning not to enter this room.

Upon entering the room, the party will notice a large hole in the north wall. In the southeast corner of the room, eleven Giant Centipedes [AC: 7, HTK: 3 each] are crawling over the mouldering corpses of three humans. One corpse has chainmail, a sword, and a pouch containing 16 gp, 25 sp, and 150 cp and an unlabeled potion (a Potion of Flying). Another, obviously female, wears platemail; a mace, a pouch containing 25 cp, clerical spell components, 2 vials of holy water, and another potion (a Potion of Love) will be found if her body is searched. On the floor next to her body is a metal scroll; it contains a contract signed by Balathor, guaranteeing at least 500 gp to each of the six members of her party, if they clean out the complex. (The contract bears a date, making it about two months old.) The third corpse, dressed in tattered robes, wears a back pack (open and empty), two rings (Fire Resistance and a normal ornate gold ring), and a small belt pouch containing a third ring (delusion).

If the party goes into the hole, they will find 8 more Giant Centipedes (AC: 7, HTK: 3 each), and will probably stumble across the body of a Gnome thief. He wears leather armor and a Ring (of Invisibility), carries three (normal) throwing daggers, and clutches another (+1) dagger in his left hand. The tunnel quickly ends. This remnant of the first party was poisoned by spiders as they slept in the "safe" area.

A trap door leads to the kitchen area on level two. The door is heavy and obviously hasn't been opened in a long time (it is spiked shut from this side).

7 Temple viewing area. The ten foot wide balcony gives a magnificent view of the temple area below (see room 5, level 3). Iron bars extend to the ceiling at nine inch intervals, protecting viewers from falling off the balcony. There are stone chairs with cushions that have rotted away. 2d4 Large Spiders [AC: 8, HTK: 6 each (1d8+1) have spun their webs in and around the iron bars. They will attack if provoked, but are not hungry (several Giant Centipedes are wrapped in the webs).

8 Spiral staircase leading down to levels 2 and 3. Every tenth stair has been replaced with woven straw dyed black to resemble the rest of the stairs. If not careful, party members must roll under their dexterity-7 on a d20 or slip and take 1d4 points of damage. Kobolds using these stairs will not collapse the false steps.

9 Stairs leading up to the basement of the tower. A single Kobold will always be on these stairs to sound an alarm if intruders are spotted (there is a 50% chance that he will faint after sounding the alarm).

10 Stairs leading down.

11 Small fountain built by dwarves. This taps an underground river and provides fresh water for the Kobolds.

FIRST LEVEL TRAPS

Most traps will be marked in advance; on the map, each trap's location is marked by a letter. Small scratches may be noted on the wall, about a foot from the floor, five feet in front and behind the trap. The scratches can be interpreted by Kobolds to show what sort of trap will be encountered. Traps that depend completely on weight will not be marked, since Kobolds can pass these without harm. If the party sets off a trap, an additional noise-making device will be set off, alerting any Kobolds within thirty feet and allowing them to attack the party while members are being extricated from a trap.

A Thin leather trip line strung eighteen inches off the ground. If a party is running by this point, the lead characters must roll under their dexterity/2 or trip (damage = 1d6 HTK). If the party is moving at normal speed, lead characters not watching for a trap must roll under their dexterity or trip (damage = 1d3 HTK). Characters making their saving throw step over the trip line. The first character to trip will usually (85%) break the trip line.

B Woven mats cover a 5'x5'x5' pit at the bottom of the staircase. The mat will collapse under the weight of a human-sized creature. There are spikes in the pit, causing 2d4 damage, save for half.

C A small board juts out from the floor and is attached to a string recessed into the stone face of the wall. If the board is moved, the "trigger" will release nets hidden on the ceiling. These nets will not cause any damage, but will entangle anyone in the square with the trigger. The board is so sensitive that even the weight of a Kobold will set off the trap; thus it is marked front and rear.

D One of the chairs in the temple veiwing area has a large iron splinter cushion. In the years since the splinter was placed by a mischevious child, it has rusted and been contaminated by the Giant Centipedes; anyone sitting on the chair must save vs. poison to avoid the splinter or get lockjaw 1d4 days later (death follows in 1d4 days).

E Mats cover the entire hallway and conceal a 5'x5'x5' pit with spikes in the bottom. Kobolds going over the section will not collapse the mats, but human-sized beings will. Damage will be 2d4, save for half damage.

DM NOTE: When the Gelatinous Cube clean-up patrols go over this area, the mats are picked up in front and replaced behind. Since the pit is only five feet deep, the Cube can pass over. Adventurers may note that the top five feet of the walls above the pit are dirtier than the rest of the walls.

FIRST LEVEL RANDOM ENCOUNTERS

Every turn roll a d6. On a 1, roll for encounter. Use the following table, rolling a d6.

1 1d4+2 unarmed Kobolds: They will surprise the party 50% of the time (due to small number) but will usually (65%) run away, attempting to warn others.

2 1d10+10 Kobold hunting party, armed with swords and spears. Will fight using normal Kobold tactics, with normal chance for surprise.

3 Gelatinous Cube tended by 2d4 hatchlings (1/3 are in front of the Cube). The Kobolds will be carrying torches and those in front will be surprised 66% of the time. The Cube will have a normal chance to surprise because of the distraction of the Kobolds. Kobolds in front of the Cube will be removing any edible material

from the floor and walls, while Kobolds behind the Cube will be herding it and resetting any traps eaten by the Cube.

4 1d4 Giant Centipedes (AC: 7, HTK: 3 each).

5 1 or 2 large, normal domesticated cats. These were originally imported for rodent control, although now they are also used in clerical rites to Morhet. They are harmless, but will surprise on 1-5 on a d6 by rubbing against party members' legs. Each will have 1d4 hits, no attack.

6 Random noise; will not attack.

SECOND LEVEL ROOMS

The rooms on this level of the dungeon were once service areas for the dwarves. Some of them have wooden service windows which can be closed and bolted. Kobolds in these rooms will be sleeping during the day and working during the night. If attacked, they will fight long enough to see they can not win, and then retreat to join other Kobolds. They will congregate in rooms marked with an asterisk (*), and attempt a mass assault as the party passes the door to their room.

1 Hunting supply room. 1d4+1 Kobolds are working on bows, arrows, and spears. The Kobolds know how to use the weapons and will do so from the window on the south part of the east wall.

2 Fishing supply room. 2d4 Kobolds are working on making fish hooks and nets. They are unarmed, but will use the nets to entangle the party, if possible.

3 Carpentry shop. One master Kobold is supervising 1d6+1 Kobolds, who are cutting wood, tying together chairs and tables, and forming crude furniture from split timbers. Carpentry tools of dwarven manufacture, worth 75 gp, are here.

4 Furrier. Three unarmed Kobolds are working here. They will hide under the furs if time permits. Any other Kobolds entering this room for an attack will also attempt to hide among the furs. There are fifteen furs worth 10d10 each in this room.

5 Laundry room. 3d6 Kobold hatchlings struggle with piles of dirty rags under the supervision of 3 Kobold officers. There is a large cistern in the south part of the west wall and four large stone vats containing water and rags sit nearby.

6 Storage room for clean clothes and laundry soap. Kobolds will hide under the clothes if running away.

7 Tailor. 2d4 Kobolds work here. There are stacks of cruddy stitched leather clothing here and many stacks of cloth which provide ideal hiding places for Kobolds.

8 Shoe and sandal shop. 1d6 Kobold cobblers work here,

making and repairing leather boots and sandals. They are armed with hammers but will run out the secret door in the southeast corner if confronted.

9 Main dining room. Four 40' long tables run the length of this room. They can each hold 60 Kobolds and will be in use most of the night. Most of the Kobolds eating here are unarmed hatchlings. They are very likely to outnumber any intruders and will attack on sight. Noises are unlikely to be heard over the din of the hall, so if battle takes place outside the dining room, Kobolds inside the hall will not be alerted. Two large swinging doors are near the north and south ends of the west wall. The two swinging doors on the north wall lead to the kitchen.

Kobold Level 2

N

scale	5 ft. ☐	steps
traps	1,2,3...	arrow slit
text ref.	A,B,C...	barrel
secret door	⑤	stacked boxes
trap door	ⓣ	chest
kobolds congregate	★	
shuttered window	❘	
cooking pit	pa	
stairwell	⊕ ▦	
statue	s	

10 Kitchen. 2d10 Kobolds work here. There is a large cooking pit in the northeast corner. Tables are scattered throughout this room for the preparation and serving of game, roots and berries, and mushrooms. The Kobolds are armed with cooking knives (equivalent to daggers for attack and damage).

A trap door, in the ceiling in the northwest portion of the room, leads up to the temple meeting area. It is spiked shut from the level above.

11 Pantry area. All six of the rooms contain foodstuffs gathered from or hunted in the forest. One of the rooms has a supply of mushrooms from the lowest level of the complex. Kobolds will be hiding here if an ambush has been arranged.

12 Second level of the temple. It is inaccessible from the second level of the complex.

13 Armorer's shop. Two Kobolds make leather armor in this room. They are not very good at it, having at most two suits in progress at any one time. They are armed with knives and will both be wearing their best armor, providing AC: 6.

14 Jewelry Shop. Two Kobolds work here, forming jewelry from silver quartz and shiny rocks. They also have hidden 14 gems (worth 20d10 gp each) in a small sack. They are unarmed and will always attempt to flee with their gems.

15 Leather Shop. 2d6 Kobolds are tanning hides and curing leather. They are armed with knives and whips (1d2 damage). A large vat of acid is in the northwest corner. Several tanned hides are hanging on the west wall.

16 Weaver's shop. 5d4 Kobolds are weaving baskets, mats, traps, and imitation stair steps. They are unarmed. Up to twelve Kobolds can hide in a pile of straw in the northeast corner of the room. Six large baskets provide cover for twelve more Kobolds in the northwest corner.

17 Hatmaker. One Kobold is making hats. There are 178 leather hats in this room. (No other Kobold wears

73

hats.)

18 Brewer. Three Kobolds are making beer. Four large kegs are fermenting in the southeast corner.

19 Spiral staircase leading up and down. Every tenth step is woven straw painted to resemble the other stairs. If not careful, adventurers must save vs. dexterity or take 1d4 damage from falling through the steps.

20 Stairway leading up to first level.

21 Stairway leading down to third level.

SECOND LEVEL TRAPS

Second level traps are marked like those on the first level.

A Trip wire 18" off the floor.

B 5'x5'x5' pits are covered with mats and contain many many sharp spikes.

C Obvious markings are scratched in the outside of this door. They are a warning, written in Kobold, not to attempt to enter this room, for the door is trapped.
   DM ONLY: There is a falling block trap built by the dwarves attached to the door. There is a false doorknob on the right side of the door and false hinges attached to the left side. The door, however, opens inward by pushing on the left side of the door. If the doorknob is pulled, it will release a lever and a 5'x5'x6" section of ceiling will fall on the person or persons in front of the door, causing 2d6 of damage. The block will quickly spring back into place, setting for the next victim. The Kobolds have not disarmed this trap, but have learned how to avoid it.

SECOND LEVEL RANDOM MONSTERS

Every turn roll 1d6. On a one, roll again on the table below.

1-3 1d6 Kobolds. They will flee in terror if not quickly subdued.
4 1 or 2 domesticated cats. They are friendly.
5 2d10 Kobolds. They will attack with short swords.
6 Random noise; will not attack.

THIRD LEVEL ROOMS

1-2 Kobold Witchdoctor's training center. During the evening, 3d6 Kobolds from 10 to 30 years old practice their spells in rooms 1 and 2. Half of the Witchdoctors are practicing first level spells in room 2; the rest are practicing second level spells in room 1 (one of these Kobolds has a Ring of Spell Turning). There are magical components in shelves on the north wall. All Kobolds in here will be dressed in robes, and will be AC: 9.

3 Morhet's temple. A circular altar dominates the northeast corner of the room. On the altar is a 5' statue of a robed and cowled female Kobold figure. There will always be 2d6 female adult Kobolds tending the incense burner and altar. The floor is covered with mats. There is a 10% chance for a ceremony for Morhet to be in progress when the temple is entered. This ceremony consists of singing, incense burning and releasing small animals through a small tunnel in the north wall behind the altar leading up to the surface. If a service is in progress, there will be 6d6 Kobolds present. They will fearlessly attack the party for violating the sanctity of Morhet's temple.

   Shamans of Morhet will be dressed in grey robes and cowls, and will be silent while conducting the service. They will not fight, but will flee when attacked. When fleeing, they will use protective spells such as Sanctuary or Hold Person. A secret trap door leading to a tunnel to the surface is hidden in the altar.

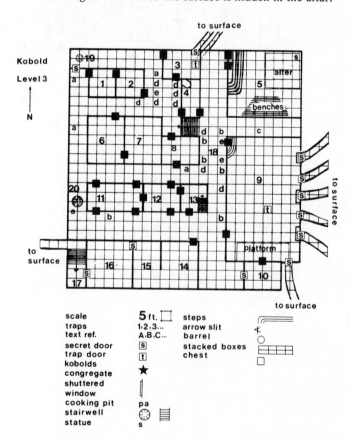

Kobold Level 3

scale	5 ft. ☐	steps
traps	1,2,3...	arrow slit
text ref.	A,B,C...	barrel
secret door	Ⓢ	stacked boxes
trap door	Ⓣ	chest
kobolds congregate	★	
shuttered window		
cooking pit	pa	
stairwell	⊕	
statue	s	

4 Farhet's temple. Four sides of a hexagonal altar protrude from the northwest corner. On the altar stands a 6' tall statue of a Kobold; he is easily weilding a 6' sword. Also on the altar is a sacrificial block with a drain running through it. The block is covered with blood and looks like it hasn't been used lately. If the party manages to get this far without letting Kobolds on this level realize it, there will not be anyone in this temple. Otherwise, a ceremony to Farhet will be occuring 25% of the time. Shamans of Farhet wear orange robes and will be armed. They can cast first and second clerical spells. The ceremony will consist of sacrifices of small animals and much shouting and

yelling. The purpose of the ceremony is to get up enough courage to attack the intruders. Participants in the rite will be so involved that there will be a four in six chance that they will be surprised.

5   Dwarven temple to Sharmal Ironfist. The area has a permanent Protection From Evil spell cast so that any evil being entering will die (evil creatures with less than 6d8 HTK are not entitled to a saving throw). Kobolds have learned the hard way not to enter the large double doors on the west side of the temple. There are many warnings, written in Kobold, along the entire east wall of the corridor outside the temple; they say, "Do not touch these doors!"

The 50' x 50' area is sunk 15' below the rest of the level. Marble steps lead from the doors down to the floor. Dominating the entire temple area is a 50' statue of Sharmal Ironfist. It was carved out of native rock as the dwarven complex was being formed. It stands on a 20' x 20' x 10' high altar in the northeast corner.

The temple area goes up through the two levels above it for a total of 55'. The south and west walls slope inward so the top of the temple is 20' x 20'. The top has a viewing area protected by iron bars (see room 7, level 1). On the altar are offerings left by the dwarves when they departed. There are three golden urns (250 gp each) that were once filled with food. A small chest on the altar is filled with 25 gems worth 100 gp each. The eyes of the statue are large diamonds worth 1000 gp each.

A colony of 15 Large Spiders [AC: 8, HTK: 6 each (1d8+1)] has taken over the area. They have spun webs over the entire statue and the pew area on the third level. They are well fed with Centipedes from the temple meeting area and will not attack unless provoked. The treasure on the altar is within the spider webs and taking it will provoke the monsters.

6   Dwarven Library. All 248 books have been stacked in a corner to make room for the Kobold male leader. He has maximum HTK (4) and AC: 6 due to high dexterity. He always has 6 guards (3 or 4 HTK each) armed with swords, accompanying him. One of the Kobold guards has a Ring of Weight. The leader has Morhet's ring. (If he uses it to teleport, he will go to the nest.)

The books are normal tomes about history, philosophy, religion, etc. The leader's large bed, in the northwest corner, has 276 gp hidden under the mattress. Six cots are along the south wall for the guards.

7   Dwarven Reading Room. This now serves as the quarters for the female leader, who serves as the head Shaman for Morhet. She will be in this room 90% of the time, in the temple 10% of the time. She has 4 HTK, a +2 Ring of Protection, and will always run away before fighting. She can cast three first and two second level clerical spells. She is attended by 4 female guards with 3 or 4 HTK each. These guards will not fight to the death, but will try to delay attackers while their leader escapes.

8   Officer's quarters. 2d8 Kobold officers are in this room. They are armed and will attack on sight. One of them has a Horn of Farhet and will use it when he sees attackers. Each officer has a chest at the foot of his cot containing clothing and 10d6 gp.

9   Dwarven meeting and lecture room. Steps lead 5' down from the large double doors in the northwest corner. The east wall is intricately carved and partly covered with woven hangings. Along the south wall is a raised area 30' long and 10' wide.

The Kobolds have turned this area into their nest. The entire floor is covered with clean straw. 300 female adult Kobolds, 38 recently hatched hatchlings, and 35 eggs are in the nest. There are 40 adult males armed with swords and spears, near the doors. In the northeast corner are 20 adult males with bows and arrows. There are 12 Boars [AC: 7, HTK: 15 each (3d8+3)], 5 Weasels [AC: 6, HTK: 12 each (3d8+3)], and 3 Otters [AC: 5, HTK: 25 each (5d8)] assisting the guards.

The Kobolds have dug five escape routes from the east wall; three are behind wall hangings, two are hidden behind carvings. Secret doors are in the easternmost part of the south wall, the southern part of the west wall, and in the middle of the floor (a trap door). The passages behind the secret doors lead up to the surface.

If the nest is attacked, the Kobold guards will attack without regard to morale until all females have escaped with the eggs and young. They will then attempt to escape. An appeal will be sent to Morhet if the guards sense defeat before the females have escaped. There is a 5% chance the appeal will be answered.

10 Dressing room for speakers. This has been turned into a private room where officers and leaders meet eligible female Kobolds. This usually involves a small donation to Morhet's temple. The walls are covered with fine cloth tapestries. The secret door in the west wall only opens from the inside and cannot be detected from the outside.

11 Dining area for leaders. A 25' long table surrounded by 16 chairs dominates the room. This room will be occupied 40% of the time by 2d8 Kobold officers, armed with swords.

12 Kitchen. 2d4 Kobold hatchlings will be preparing food. They are unarmed and will run away if possible.

   DM NOTE: If the party checks the large pile of bones in one corner, they will find the skulls of the last two members of the first expeditionary force.

13 Food storage area. Stairs lead down into a 50' x 90' area. Fungi and lichen are cultivated in this area and turned into a gruel for consumption in the dining areas on the second and third levels. An escape tunnel runs from the west end of the lower area up to the forest above.

DM NOTE: The following rooms belong to Aspregull the Strict, the founder of the city of Aspregull, who left the area some 650 years ago (see the explanation of Aspregull in the Introduction).

14 Human Magic Users workshop. The door to the entrance is wizard-locked. In front of the door are the bones of six Kobolds that have been dead for more than two years. Across from the door on the south wall is a Caryatid Column [AC: 5, HTK: 22]. The column has the permanent ability to Detect Evil, (since the magic-user created the column by using some of his own blood, the Permanency spell could be cast on it) and has been commanded to prevent any being an evil nature from entering the workshop and quarters. Furthermore, if any non-evil creatures enter, it has been instructed to lead them to the west end of the north wall and show them the notice etched into the stone.

   The notice welcomes the creatures to the workshop of Aspregull the Strict. He is out at the moment, but invites any good creatures to stay as long as they wish. It also welcomes magic-users of good alignment to use the books and items in this and the next room, but warns that anyone committing an evil or chaotic act while possessing any of the items will be cursed. (This is true. The curse will cause the user to donate 75% of his wealth immediately to the nearest lawful good temple, and to continue donating 75% of any future wealth for one year or until the item is returned, which whichever is longer.) Also, the items must be returned within one week of their loan or they will teleport back to this room, and the curse will take effect. (DM: Aspregull often loaned items to the dwarves, but did not want them to get "lost." Since they were magicked to return to the workshop, Aspregull left them behind.)

Tables in this room hold equipment (balances, pestles, and mortars, very sharp crystal knives, etc.) and withered, unuseable components. There are twelve chairs scattered around three tables; a thick coating of dust covers everything. A cabinet in the northwest corner contains several reference books.

15 Magic-users library and study. Bookshelves line the east wall. A rolltop desk is in the southwest corner. A false door is on the west wall in the north part. (Behind the false door is a secret door leading into Aspregull's quarters.)

   The bookshelves contain eight spell books, six history books, a diary, seventeen natural history books, and several empty books of a non-magical nature. The spell books each contain all magic-user spells of a particular level, but cannot be opened without knowing the word that locked them. (Saying the names of the Sun and the Moon will open the first and second level books, respectively, while saying the names of the six innermost planets will open the third through eighth level books.) Knock spells will not work on the books; if they are forced open, the pages will disintegrate.

   The history books are in Aspregull's handwriting (same as the notice on the wall).

   The diary is written in code, but the dates reveal the book to be 700 years old.

   In the desk are several items. In the first drawer are writing quills, parchment, and an inkwell. In the second drawer are three scrolls; one contains a Web spell, the second a Magic Missile spell, and the last an Invisibility spell. DM ONLY: All the scrolls are at 17th level. Casting the spells will not curse the caster as described above).

   In the bottom drawer are three items. There is a +2 Ring of Protection, a Wand of Paralyzation, and a Gem of True Seeing. DM ONLY: Each item is correctly labeled and cursed as described in 14 above.

16 Aspregull's personal quarters. There is a large bed in the southwest corner, a dresser next to it along the west wall. A crystal ball sits on a stand in the southeast corner of the room. The dresser contains normal clothes and robes.

17 Aspregull's escape route. A steep staircase leads down and west from the north end of the room; it eventually surfaces in the forest 3/4 of a mile away.

18 Stairway leading up. A coat room between the temple and the meeting hall has 30 pegs on the north and south walls. There are 15 cloaks hanging there.

19 Spiral staircase leading up. Every tenth step is woven straw pointed black to resemble the stairs. If the party is not careful, they will fall through taking 1d4 damage.

20 A cistern tapped into an underground river.

THIRD LEVEL TRAPS

This entire level is covered with mats.

A Trip wire 18" from the ground.

B 10' pit under the mat. Spikes are in the bottom of the pit, causing 4d4 damage; save vs. death for half damage.

C Pressure plate attached to nets that are rigged to drop on the party.

D Large stone chest; locked and protected by a Leomund's trap. The chest is empty.

E 20' pit under mat. 3d6 HTK damage; save vs. death for half damage.

THIRD LEVEL RANDOM MONSTERS

Roll 1d6 every three turns. On a one, roll again and consult the table below. Kobolds encountered will attack and try to warn the nest about intruders.

1 2d6 adult Kobolds armed with swords and spears.

2 2d4 Shamans of Farhet armed with clubs, accompanied by 1d12 adult Kobolds armed with swords. Half the Shamans can use only first level spells while the rest can use first and second level spells.

3 1d4 Shamans of Morhet. Will flee if possible.

4 1d6 Witchdoctors with 2d4 guards.

5 3d4 females accompanied by 2d6 males. Females will flee while males delay party.

6 Random noise. Will not attack.

GOBLINS AND HOBGOBLINS

by Sue Khas

HISTORY AND ORIGIN

The creation of Goblins and Hobgoblins is shrouded in mystery. Many legends exist, but even the Elven Archivists cannot agree on what might be the truth. One legend relates that the Goblins races were created by the Gnome god, Larglar, to be servants for his nation of Gnomes (though Gnome Sages deny this). Another legend tells of the Arch Mage Gygorix who swept across the continent in 400,000 BP (before present) with a hoard of "foul, multicolored gobbling creatures" destroying all who dared resist them. He was defeated at long last by the race he feared least (the Halflings), whereupon his creatures disappeared into the Black Wyvern Mountains. Corroboration for this event exists in Halfling history, but the exact nature of Gygorix's creatures was not recorded. A third legend, discoverd in a tome in the Linorian Archives, relates that the Goblins were created for three witch sisters by the demon they served.

Despite their disparity, all the legends agree upon one point, that Goblinkind was created when water from the Well of Life was poured upon colored lumps of clay from the caverns in the Lost Mountain. The Goblin races evidently agree, for the Lost Mountain is revered as their most holy spot; all hope it will be rediscovered before they are recalled to their god.

Due to their prodigious birth rate and evil nature, the Goblin races have come close to overunning the civilized lands of the world on several occasions. Each time, the other races, fearing extinction, retaliated by systematically exterminating them. Despite these efforts, Goblinkind still flourishes.

GOBLINKIND

The Goblin races are all humanoid in appearance. They range in color from browns, greens, and greys, to dull reds and muted oranges, and have large glowing red eyes, flat faces, and long, sharp fangs well-suited for rending flesh from bone. During the winter, and in harsher climates, they are covered with a thick bristly fur which affords some protection from the cold.

GOBLINS

Goblins are 4 to 4½' tall, and have 1d8-1 HTK. Their skin is extremely sensitive to the drying effects of both the sun and the wind and is often chapped and cracked. To prevent this painful condition from occuring, the Goblins remain underground as much as possible and smear themselves liberally with animal fats and oils; this gives them a permanent rancid odor. Hobgoblins do not suffer from this problem.

Goblins prefer loose garments that do not inhibit their movement (or irritate their skin), and are usually clad in a loincloth, baggy pants and a long knee-length shift. Strips of leather are used to hold the shift in place, criss-crossing across the chest and back and belted about the waist. They wear high leather boots, leather helmets reinforced with metal and, when engaged in battle, bracers. Females only wear small loincloths, for they are continually tending the crops and nursing their young in their subterranean homes. Since they seldom venture outside and never engage in combat, clothing is seen as superfluous.

Goblins dislike sunlight and will usually be encountered only after the sun has set. When encountered in full sunlight, they will be at a -1 to hit and damage. If encountered by day, they will be 1d10 in number, while by night, they will be 4d100 strong.

For every 50 Goblins encountered, there will be one Clan Elder, 5 Clan Leaders, a Shaman, and 2 Witchdoctors. There is a 50% chance that 1/3 of the party encountered will be mounted on 4d8 HTK Dire Wolves. Further, for every 200 encountered, there will also be a War Chief and 1d20 guards. If a War Chief is present (65% chance), he will usually be a Hobgoblin, If this is the case, the Goblins will fight using Hobgoblin tactics (refer to the next section for War Chief's stats).

Clan Elders have 2d8-2 HTK; Clan Leaders have 2d8-4 HTK; Guards have 3d8-3 HTK; and War Chiefs, if Goblin, have 4d8-4 HTK. Elders, Leaders and Guards each have a 20% chance of owning a +1 weapon. A War Chief has a 60% chance of owning a +1 weapon, 1 30% chance of owning a +2 weapon, and a 10% chance of owning a +3 or better weapon; they also have a 10% chance of owning magical armor and/or shield. Witchdoctors and Shamans are armed only with daggers and clubs, relying primarily upon their spell-casting abilities. Unlike other Goblins, they stay toward the rear of battles to cast their spells in safety. Witchdoctors have one additional HTK for every level they have attained, while Shamans have 1d4 additional HTK.

HOBGOBLINS

Hobgoblins stand 6-7' tall and have 1d8+1 HTK. Hobgoblins prefer heavier clothing and are usually clad in several layers of pants and shirts covered by a leather vest. Being colorblind, their choice of clothing is based on the pattern rather than the color of the cloth. Thus, they often present a ludicrous sight. Few laugh at them openly for they have a fearsome reputation as fighters. They wear knee-high leather boots that contain metal reinforcements to provide additional protection in battle. They wear both gauntlets and bracers and have a fondness for unusual helmets. Many Hobgoblin helmets sport great horns and other battle mementoes, while other helmets are taken from the slain bodies of adversaries. (This passion for headgear is so intense, that they will often attack a party just to obtain a helmet that they fancy.)

Hobgoblins, accustomed to sunlight are always encountered in groups numbering 2d100. For every 20 encountered there will be 1 Clan Elder, 2 Clan Leaders, 1 Witchdoctor and 1 Shaman. If over 100 are encountered, there will be an additional 5 Clan Elders, 5 Clan Leaders, and a War Chief with 2d20 guards, 5 additional Witchdoctors and 8 additional Shamans. Clan Elders have 3d8+3 HTK, Clan Leaders have 2d8+2 HTK, and have a 5% chance of owning a +1 weapon. Hobgoblin guards have 4d8+4 HTK, a 10% chance of owning a +1 weapon, and a 15% chance of owning magical armor and shield. A Hobgoblin War Chief, with 5d8+5 HTK, has a 25% chance of owning a +1 weapon, a 15% chance of owning a +2 weapon, a 5% chance of owning a +3 or better weapon and a 5% chance of owning magical armor and/or shield.

Hobgoblin Witchdoctors and Shamans are identical to their Goblin cousins in weapons used, tactics employed and

vital statistics. Witchdoctors and Shamans of Goblinkind do not wear armor or carry shields. They are usually clad in fur robes.

SKILLS

GOBLINS

Goblins are fair miners and stoneworkers. They have a 25% chance of spotting sloping passages, new construction, secret doors, and panels carved of natural rock. They are lazy and unambitious and only engage in mining when slaves are available to do most of the work. They are skilled leather workers and masters at distilling poisons.

They manufacture leather goods of very high quality, but do not decorate them with patterns or designs. Traders pay top prices for these sought-after items, and, through a number of intermediaries, sell them to unsuspecting humans.

The manufacture of poisons is the responsibility of the Witchdoctor who oversees the gathering of the components by the members of the tribe and the preparation of the poison by his assistants. The poisons fall into three major categories; insinuative, ingestive, and contact.

INSINUATIVE POISONS are primarily used in warfare, and several types are manufactured. First and most favored, is KALMARATA, a poison manufactured from the joice of the nettle plant. Kalmarata is used to coat arrows and darts. It disables the victim by causing severe cramping muscle spasms and paralysis within 1d4 rounds. This poison is not fatal, but its effects last for 20 days, minus 1 day per point of stamina. If the antidote, made from the pulp of freshly mashed caterpillers, is administered, the effects will only last for 20 hours, minus 1 hour per point of constitution. ARTELIROG, a poison manufactured from the dried fibers of rheubarb plant roots, causes the victim to suffer from diahrrea, vomiting, chills, uncontrollable shakes, and eventually death. The onset of the effects varies widely, taking from as little as a minute to over an hour (1d100 minute). Artelirog is often used to coat the blades of hand-held weapons. There is no known natural antidore, and a neutralize poison is needed to save the victim. PARSELISI, on the other hand, is a fast-acting poison which causes the heartrate to accelerate ten-fold; heart will burst within 1d12 rounds. This poison can be readily countered by the ingestion of any compound that slows heartrate, a Slow spell, or a clerical Slow Poison spell. The last poison of this type is the SZAPPANOR, which causes temporary blindness lasting 1d10 turns.

Two different CONTACT POISONS are produced by the Goblins: CSELIBAR, often used on the chains and locks of slaves causes, intense blistering of the skin within 1d4 minutes of contact. Unless it is immediately washed off permanent scarring will result. FATTYAR causes tissue in the affected area to degenerate rapidly, causing 1d4 points of damage per round for up to six rounds until it is neutralized.

INGESTED POISONS, seldom used by the Goblin races, are produced as trade goods. KALTISO is a quick,

painless poison which causes the victim to fall into a deep coma. SEVERAG, a honey colored brew extracted from Water Hyacinth bulbs and Kumquat pits, is extremely deadly, causing death in 1d4 rounds. ITSORAL, a greenish powder prepared form the unripe fruit of the wild Lippa Melon, is a slow acting poison which is typically administered over a period of days or weeks. It causes the victim to experience headaches, blurred vision, vomiting and diarrhea. Small welts often appear across the chest and throat of the victim; these are often misdiagnosed as plague. Death occurs when an individual receives a critical dose, usually between 4 to 5 tablespoonfuls.

HOBGOBLINS

Hobgoblins are better stoneworkers than Goblins, despite the fact that they live above the ground. They are not as lazy as the Goblins, and excavate extensively beneath their dwellings to provide safe areas should they be attacked. They have the same detection abilities as Goblins, but at 30%.

Unlike Goblins, Hobgoblins have never mastered the art of leatherworking, and rely on Goblin trade for their needs. In turn, they supply Goblins with weapons, primarily short swords, long swords, and spears. They also manufacture two-handed swords and halberds for their own use, and occasionally trade these items to other Dark Races. The quality of Hobgoblin workmanship is not very good, and the percentage of weapon breakage is high (2% per round). Despite this, Hobgoblins prefer weapons of their own manufacture. They also fashion sturdy metal and wood shields, both large and small.

ARMOR AND WEAPONS

GOBLINS

Due to their small stature, Goblins favor the following relatively light-weight weaponry and armor:

20% Leather Armor, Small Shield, and Spear
20% Animal Skin Armor, Small Shield, Sling, and Flail
30% Leather Armor, Flail, Small Shield
10% Studded Leather, Small Shield, Short Sword, and Spear
20% Leather Armor, Small Shield, Short Sword, and Darts

HOBGOBLINS

Towering over Goblins both in size and weight, Hobgoblins favor larger and heavier weapons and armor:

10% Chainmail Armor, Large Shield, Bastard Sword, and Spear
20% Chainmail Armor, Small Shield, Longsword, and Heavy Crossbow
20% Scale Mail Armor, 2-handed Battleaxe, and Heavy Crossbow
20% Chainmail Armor, Small Shield, 2-Handed Sword, and Spear
30% Chainmail Armor, Large Shield, and Halberd

FIGHTING STYLE

GOBLINS

Goblins are straightforward fighters, preferring a full frontal attack after first discharging their missile weapons to weaken the opposition. They will use any obvious terrain advantages offered by the surrounding land, but will not hold off an attack until the enemy is in a less defensible position.

They lack any real skill at military planning or tactics and rely primarily on overwhelming numbers to win a battle. They are fierce fighters and rarely retreat; when their numbers are depleted by three quarters, the survivors undergo a berserker rage, discarding their shields in favor of maneuverability. This total disregard for their own safety gives them a bonus of +3 to hit and +1 to damage.

HOBGOBLINS

Hobgoblins, not bothered by sunlight, often attack during the daylight hours. They are formidable fighters and military tacticians. Unlike Goblins, they do not mindlessly charge to the attack, but deploy their forces for optimum advantage. They will lure their adversaries into ambushes, encircle them, and cut off their retreat. Their favorite tactic is to separate the opposition into small groups by having mounted units of Hobgoblin cavalry attack in short, fast rushes. They then retreat slowly drawing some opposition with them. The main Hobgoblin fighting force will then cut off and decimate each separate group. Recognizing the danger from mages, Hobgoblins will immediately attempt to kill or disable them, usually from ambush before the fighting commences. If there is a safe chance of capturing a cleric alive, Hobgoblins will attempt to do so in order to sacrifice him to their gods. If not, clerics receive the same attention as mages.

TRIBAL LIFE AND HIERACHY

Both Goblin races are highly tribal in nature, with a strictly maintained pecking order. Laws and regulations are tightly enforced and severe punishments are meted out to any transgressors. Any individual shirking his responsibilities will be immediately brought before the chief and his Elders for justice. Very few transgressors are given the opportunity to break the law a second time, for the death penalty is meted out for the most trivial of transgressions.

Laws governing daily life vary from tribe to tribe and village to village. Newcomers must be wary, for ignorance of local laws does not absolve the transgressor of his crime, nor lessen his punishment. Transgressions not requiring the death penalty are not treated lightly; other punishments include being stripped of all rank within the tribe, loss of all property (this includes females and offspring), loss of all rights, and relegation to a life as a bond-slave to the Chieftain's females. The last is considered to be the most cruel and demeaning of punishments. Those sentenced to life-long servitude invariably plead for death.

Although both the Goblins and Hobgoblins have titular Monarchs, neither is very powerful. The Monarchs are chosen for a lifetime of service from among the Chiefs of all the tribes on the basis of strength, cunning, and repute. Once chosen, the Monarch's tribe enjoys a certain amount of prestige, but has very little actual control over other tribes. Each Goblin tribe also has a Hobgoblin Overlord, a hereditary leader with no actual control except in times of war. Then the Goblin races unite to face the common enemy and threat of extermination under the leadership of the Monarch and the Overlords.

Among the Goblin races, the Tribal Chieftain is the sole head of the fighting forces, and rules in the day-to-day matters of the tribe. The Chieftain is second in power only to the Shaman and dictates in all matters other than warfare. Assisting the Tribal Chieftain are a number of Tribal Leaders who are responsible for overseeing the manufacture of weapons and armor, and Tribal Elders who are responsible for training all tribe members in fighting skills. Both Elders and Leaders are responsible for enforcing the laws of the tribe and are aided in this task by the Chief's guards and their own handpicked force of deputies.

Although Monarchs are elected, Chieftains are not, and the method of their selection reflects on the highly competitive nature of the race as well as their ongoing struggle for rulership by the fittest. Four times a year, when the seasons change, a Tribal Chieftain may be "challenged" by any other member of the tribe. These challenges include bare-handed combat, weapon combat, and assassination attempts. All contenders spend the week prior to the challenge night eliminating the other competitors (these competitions are not usually to the death). The time limit for the challenges is strictly enforced and is limited to one night, between sunset and sunrise. Neither Chieftain nor contender may have assistance in any fight and the victor is unanimously proclaimed Chief. If the challenger has not killed or subdued the curent Chief by sunrise, the Chief has retained his position. Such a chaotic system insures that the Chieftain does not become lax and weak; he must continually prove that he is the most cunning and strongest member of the tribe.

HOBGOBLIN RULE OVER GOBLINS AND GOBLIN-HOBGOBLIN RACE RELATIONS

Since their creation, Goblins and Hobgoblins have remained close allies. At any time, it is 90% likely that Goblins will be visiting in a Hobgoblin settlement, and the reverse also holds true. After the first mass extermination of Goblinkind, a bond of mutual need brought them closer. The Goblins, decimated due to their lack of tactical skills, asked the Hobgoblins for training in strategy. The Hobgoblins obliged and soon discovered that while Goblins were hellacious fighters, they were incapabile of learning even the most fundamental of military tactics.

For many years thereafter, Goblins were ruled solely by Hobgoblins (they were allowed to participate in Goblin Chieftain challenges). During the Second War of Goblinkind, the Hobgoblins led the Goblins in a fierce fight. After their defeat, the Goblins realized that they had been being utilized as cannon fodder by the Hobgoblins. During the ensuing years of relative peace, the Goblins decided that while Hobgoblin assistance was still needed, they would not be ruled by Hobgoblins. The Hobgoblins, depleted in numbers, accepted this change and a new tradition was born. Each year, following the Hobgoblin Chieftain challenges, a number of Hobgoblin chiefs are ousted from their position of responsibility. Rather than remain with their old tribe, these former leaders often travel the lands offering their services to Goblin tribes as War Chieftains. This works to the advantage of both races, for the Goblins gain skilled military and tactical leadership and the Hobgoblins are able to maintain control of the Goblin fighting forces through the War Chiefs. The Third War of Goblinkind proved the relationship to be successful, for the Goblin races were fiercer than in the past. Humankind, close to defeat near the end of the War, used a Hobgoblin tactic, the ambush, to snatch victory from the jaws of defeat.

RACE RELATIONS, ALLIANCES, AND RIVALRIES

Goblins have an intense hatred of all subterranean races with whom they vie for living space. They maintain themselves in a constant state of readiness to attack any vulnerable subterranean complex. The large well-deveoped tunnel complexs excavated by Dwarves and Gnomes are constantly sought after by Goblins. Gnomish and Dwarven prisoners and slaves are highly prized by Goblins and a brisk trade exists between Goblins and slavers. The Goblins purchase these slaves with poisons and leather goods, which are in turn sold by the slavers in far off lands where their apparent source is not readily known. Dwarves raid Goblin complexes in order to free slaves and often fall victim to Goblin ambushes set to trap such parties. Raiders that enter these foul lairs aften discover to their dismay, that Goblins use the deaths of slaves to cover their retreat (see section on Homes, below).

A special hatred exists between Goblins and Halflings. This hatred lends support to the legend that the Goblin

communal living areas surrounded by many smaller chambers that house the Witchdoctors, Shamans, Elders, Leaders, Guards, and the Chieftain.

Goblin dwellings have no formal furnishings. The rock floors are covered with woven plant mats, piles of furs serve as bedding, and personal possessions are stored in great leather satchels, wooden crates, and chests. The common areas contain firepits are for cooking, benches and tables for eating and a large number of Dire Wolves. The air is filled with nauseating mixture of the smells of cooking food, rotting vegetation, and offal.

Slaves are kept near the entrance to the tunnel complex and are used as a delaying tactic should the complex be invaded. The ceiling above their stalls is riddled with holes. If the complex is invaded, the guards tip over several large barrels of oil that are placed on a ledge above the main body of the stalls, and within 1-4 minutes the unfortunate slaves are soaked. The guards then set fire to the oil and flee down the corridor to warn the tribe.

Family life, as known among civilized races, is non-existent. Females are the property of the tribe, and mating occurs randomly. When a female becomes pregnant, each male who has mated with her in the past month is summoned by the Shaman to sit in the Circle of Ownership. All newly impregnated females participate in the same ceremony; often, several hundred males are invited to the ceremony. The females prepare food for the men, each dropping a distinctive pebble in one of the portions of food. After a formal ritual conducted by the Shaman, each male selects a plate of food. The males who discover pebbles are declared to be fathers. Upon the cub's birth, it becomes his property, though the female continues to care for it. Caring for one male's child does not prohibit the female from further liasons, and it is common to find a female caring for the offspring of at least a half-a-dozen males at the same time.

HOBGOBLINS

Hobgoblins do not share the Goblin craving for life below ground. They prefer living in great defensible forts and villages—after the original inhabitants have been exterminated. Great care is taken not to destroy crops when taking over a settlement, for the Hobgoblins rely on the conquered peoples' food supplies to tide them through the next winter. Hobgoblins are competent farmers and the females spend much time raising crops while the men are hunting or tunneling. The males still maintain and perfect their mining techniques, using them in the construction of escape tunnels beneath their villages.

Conquered villages and settlements are lived in until they fall apart from lack of repair, for Hobgoblins possess neither the skill nor the interest to perform such activity. Homes are furnished only if the original occupants left furniture behind. Otherwise, the rooms contain piles of skins, split logs, and crude animal skin hammocks nailed to the walls. Recognizing the need to maintain their weapons, the smithy of the settlement is rebuilt, if needed, and put into operation. Hobgoblin smiths produce items of less-than-average quality, and are constantly searching for a skilled slave to supervise. Once the village crumbles about them, Hobgoblins pick up their possessions and move on in search of a new home. This Hobgoblin migration usually

races are the descendants of the creatures of Gygoriax, though oddly enough, Hobgoblins are neutral toward Halflings. This disparity in attitude is the only source of dissention between Goblins and Hobgoblins. Typically, Hobgoblins respond by saying that Halflings, small, weak, and insignificant, are not worthy of their attention.

The Goblin races are neither closely allied nor openly hostile toward the other Dark Folk, with one exception—Orcs. Orcs are viewed as loathsome, vile, and despicable creatures to be slaughtered at every opportunity. This hatred dates back countless generations to a time when the Orcs and Goblinkind were allies against an invasion of Frost Giants. The Goblin races claim that during the final confrontation, the Orcs switched allegiances and led the Goblins into a Giant ambush. Although the Orcs deny this, they are unable to explain why their overlord bears the title, Right Arm of Karad (Karad was the leader of the Giant forces in the subject battle).

HOMES AND FAMILY RELATIONSHIPS

Goblins live exclusively in underground caves. Although they are good miners, they are extremely lazy and do not usually bother with any major modifications to a city captured from another race. When forced to excavate a new complex, their lairs consist of a number of large

occurs in the spring after the crops are planted (after all, they may be forced back to their original settlement).

RELIGION AND THE GODS

The Goblin races worship the three daughters of a Demon Prince—Elishardia the Pain-Giver, Chelethiara the Venomed-One, and Brozhanna the Vile-hearted. These three sisters plotted the destruction of their sire, and, failing, were cast out from the Nether plane to wander the lands with mortals. For centuries they roamed the land seeking worshippers through whose sacrifices they could regain their power. In time, they discovered the evil Goblin races, eliminated their Monarchs, and established an iron-fisted grip on all Goblinkind.

Daily sacrifices of demi-humans and humans quickly replenished their powers. In turn, they were not unkind to their worshippers, for they taught them the arts of torture, deceit, and poison making. As the power of the evil trio grew, so did the power of the Shamans. The Shamans, in turn, spurred the tribes on to greater deeds of slaughter thereby insuring that their power would continue to grow.

When the sisters fully regained their power and returned to the Nether Plane, they no longer ruled directly, but expressed their wishes through the Shamans. In return for exceptional service, Shamans were occasionally called to serve the goddesses, and in time they too gained worshipers among the tribes. The Demon goddesses did not object to this development for these demi-gods in turn sacrificed much of their power to them.

ELISHADRA, THE PAIN-GIVER

AC: 2
HTK: 179
Stats: 19, 21, 21, 20, 20, 4

Elishadra appears in the guise of an aged crone. Her face is covered with warts, boils, and ulcers, the nails on her claw-like hands are long and browned with age, and her body and clothing are filthy and crawling with lice and other vermin. She delights in slow-torture and inflicting much pain. She attacks twice per round with her razor-sharp nails that do 5-20 HTK damage each. After each successful hit, her victim must save vs. paralysis at -3 or become catatonic for 3-12 days!

She rides a lesser demon named Datamar [AC: 1, HTK: 22 (5d8), 1 attack for 3-12 plus poison], a many legged spider steed who has the ability to assume the shape of any humanoid. He often uses his shape-changing ability to lure victims to his mistress, but has no effective attacks when using this power.

Elishadra cannot be killed on this Plane. Her soul is secreted in a gem which is hidden on the Nether Plane beneath the throne of the Demon Prince. Only if the gem is shattered can she be permanently killed. If reduced to 0 or less HTK, she will be forced to return to the Nether Plane and remain there for 12d12 days.

CHELITIARA, THE VENOMED-ONE

AC: 3
HTK: 125
Stats: 24, 19, 19, 19, 19, 11

Chelethiara can appear in the guise of any venomous creature. In her true form, she is a giant snake from the waist down and female from the waist up. One of her favorite ploys is to hide her snake half in tall grasses or bushes near the side of a road while leaving her human torso exposed on the ground in the attitude of a faint. When an unsuspecting victim bends over her, her snake body coils about him while she injects him with her venom. Her bite is not immediately deadly. It will sap one point of random characteristic from the victim per day until he dies. There is no saving throw allowed for the effects of the poison; if a Neutralize Poison spell is cast, the victim must make his save vs. poison at -2 in order to be cured, a Slow Poison spell will have no effect.

Three times per day, she can spit a concentrated venom (-5 to save) which kills instantly (if saved, it halves victim's maximum number of HTK). She can be harmed only by edged weapons.

If reduced to 0 HTK, Chelethiara will teleport to the Nether Plane. She will remember those who fought her and will attempt to seek them out in their sleep nightly by dream walking. This innate ability allows her to walk in the dreams of all sleepers unseen, though her presence is often felt in the form of a nightmare. When she succeeds (15% chance per night, non-cumulative), she will bite her victim and teleport away, thereby visiting a long, lingering death upon her enemy.

BORZSANNA, THE VILE-HEARTED

AC: 0
HTK: 115
Stats: 18, 21, 19, 17, 19, 25

Borzsanna's evil heart is hidden behind her beautiful exterior. She appears as a young innocent human maiden of tender years. Weaker in attributes than her sisters, she is probably the evilest and cruelest of the three and is certainly the wiliest. Like her sister Elishardia, she is immune to death on this plane, for her soul is stored in a gem resting at the bottom of the Well of Life. Thus, she fears neither man nor beast. If reduced to 0 or less HTK, she will be forced to return to the Nether Plane and remain there for 10d12 days.

She is the sower of discord, the harbinger of malcontent, the green flame of jealousy, and the queen of averice. She spreads her evil in the form of a kiss which permanently imbues her victim with one of the qualities for which she is known (On a 1d4, her victim is imbued with discord; on a 2 with malcontent, on 3 with jealousy, and on 4 with averice.) The unwary victim is not entitled to a saving throw if the kiss is accepted freely. Once she has visited her evil on an individual, she will remain to watch her victim deteriorate into a creature driven by his desires. Unlike her sisters, she carries a small dagger called Sword Brother, which on command will transform into a +2 sword. She is a skill 11 swordswoman.

THE DEMIGODS

There have been many demigods chosen from the Goblin races. Shilgartor, Trasgnorl, Froltigar, Zrogvol, Quiorom, Aphasid, and many others are worshipped in day-day-to-day matters. A Shaman can contact a demi-god (through fasting and meditation) in order to gain his assistance in overcoming enemies (a troublesome Chieftain, for instance). The Shaman may also attempt to join forces spiritually with the demi-god in times of great need. If successful, this joining will add the powers of the demi-god to those of the Shaman. These powers include: Dimension Door, Double Power Charm, Flame Strike, and Charm Plants. There is only a 5% chance (per level of Shaman) that any attempt will be successful. The joining lasts for 1 day for each level of the Shaman. Upon termination, there is 40% chance that the Shaman will be whisked to the spirit plane to serve the demi-god and, as a result, this power is reserved for emergencies.

WITCHDOCTORS AND SHAMANS

Witchdoctors are the healers of Goblinkind, practicing both god-given and natural healing skills. They gather a variety of plants, roots, mosses, and other healing herbs and manufacture non-magical curative poultices and potions for the tribe. Those injuries that cannot be cured by ordinary means are often cured with spells. Goblins also purchase magical healing potions from Trolls, trading fruit, bitter roots, and weapons for the potions.

Because the Witchdoctor wields power over life and death, they are accorded a great deal of respect, and are usually the wealthiest individuals in the tribe. They are also the most vulnerable, for when a cure is not effective, the family of the patient will probably attack the Witchdoctor. Moreover, a Witchdoctor who fails to curry favor with either Chieftain or Shaman will quickly find himself on an altar being readied for sacrifice.

Shamans, relying on intelligence, not strength, select apprentices from the mature male offspring in the tribe. The selection ceremony, held every five years, is very secret; only the youth and the Shamans attend. Not all the youth return from the ceremony, and the others never speak of what transpired. Usually, the apprentice Shamans chosen are the youths that achieved the highest acclaim during the ceremony of adulthood. For the next twelve months they are subjected to further aptitude tests. This testing often takes the form of absolute servility to the

Shamans rather than any real examination of their actual intelligence. In any case, the youngster must attend the Shamans, for being selected is a great honor, and any who abrogate responsibility are summarily executed. At the end of the first year, one or two apprentices are chosen to become assistant Shamans.

The workload of the assistant Shamans is staggering. In addition to mastering spell-casting techniques and learning to brew poisons, they must willingly assist any other Shaman in the tribe for whatever period is requested. It is not surprising to find that many assistant Shamans spend 12-16 years in servitude before achieving the status of Shaman.

Upon the death of the Head Shaman, a contest of power is held among the Shamans to determine who will assume the mantle of leadership. It is not unusual for a number of Shamans to die during this ceremonial struggle for power.

Shamans are the direct voices of the gods and as such command obedience from all. Those with average intelligence (6-10) are able to achieve skill 4, those with an intelligence of over 11 are able to rise as high as the 7th level of skill.

THE ILLARIAN FOREST INTRIGUE

INTRODUCTION FOR THE DM

This adventure was designed for a relatively high level party, i.e., 6-8 players of 5th-8th levels. You may include higher level characters at your discretion, for the adventure has the potential to be quite deadly. All Goblins love to manufacture and use poisons, and those to be encountered are no exception; there is a 65% chance that any weapon used by an ordinary Goblin will be envenomed, and a 100% chance for weapons wielded by elders and leaders.

Since the party is likely to encounter wandering monsters on the trip to the caverns and on the second level of the caverns, encounter tables have been provided. They are located at the end of the adventure.

INTRODUCTION FOR THE PLAYERS

While travelling through the beautiful Illarian Forest, you meet a small patrol of Elves. As it is getting late, they invite you to share their hospitality at the capital, not far from where you are about to camp. They seem most anxious to have you accompany them, telling you that it is not often they have travellers in their part of the world, and make the offer so enticing that it is impossible to resist.

Arriving in the capital of Illaria, you discover that the entire city, built high in the branches of giant redwood trees, is all but invisible from the ground. The Elves sound a whistle, a number of cages are lowered, and you are hoisted up to the city. You are indeed wined and dined and have a most enjoyable evening—just as had been promised.

Late that night, as you are entering the Grey Mist Inn

to enjoy some much needed sleep, an extremely old Elf, dressed in simple but elegant gown, appears and introduces himself as one of the Sage Elders. He begs your indulgence, apologizes for disturbing you, and says that he has great need of your services. He asks that you accompany him to the Council of Sages. Considering the hospitality the Elves have shown, you accompany him without any hesitation.

The Illarian Elves, dedicated to scholarly pursuits, have little contact with outsiders except for their yearly caravans to Jovian Falls, where they trade tomes of knowledge for needed supplies. The Kingdom of Illaria spans 3,600 square miles, most of it virgin forest. Beside the capital of Illaria, there are only twelve small settlements in the entire area. These settlements serve as observation posts for sages pursuing studies requiring solitude and quiet observation; they seldom have a population exceeding 15 inhabitants.

The capital is the home of 4,000 Elves. Citizenship in Illaria is more a matter of embracing the scholarly life than accident of birth, and the kingdom is a melting pot of many Elven Races. An elaborate system of rope bridges connects the houses to the various institutions and, as a result, the Elves seldom leave the safety of their lofty homes.

The Kingdom has enjoyed peace and prosperity since its earliest days. Recently, that peace was broken when a tribe of Goblins, led by their Hobgoblin Cheiftain settled in Illaria. For several years, the arrival of the tribe had no appreciable effect on the lives of the Elves; they seldom ventured from their tree homes, and the Goblins stayed ensconced in their caverns. In the past year, however, the Goblins and Hobgoblins have multiplied so rapidly that in their search for food, they have destroyed massive areas of the forest, driven off and massacred the game, polluted the rivers, and destroyed the peaceful harmony of the land.

The Elves attempted to negotiate with the Goblins and their leaders, but after numerous outrages, they conceded that no agreement could be reached. In recent months, large parties of Goblins and Hobgoblins have attacked Elven homes and settlements; those whom they did not kill, they took as slaves. The yearly caravan to Jovian Falls was attacked, and of the 60 Elves travelling with the caravan, only 1 survived.

That Elf, Finseer Falcon-Brother, escaped after several months of slavery and made his way to the capital. He reported that the Goblins, numbering in the thousands, were planning to unify all the Goblin tribes of the continent under the leadership of Csarglargar, the Horned Shaman and Zaabrol Fire-Eater, the Hobgoblin Chieftain. From scraps of conversation that he overheard, he learned that some great discovery had been made in the Watery Caverns. The Goblins believed it would enable them to form a nation of Goblinkind. Unfortunately, he was unable to learn the nature of the discovery. On the night of his escape, several thousand Goblin envoys left to carry the news of the discovery to the other tribes.

The news of an impending Goblin Nation so greatly

disturbed the Elves that they immediately sent several messengers to Jovian Falls requesting assistance. Their bodies were found, torn and mutilated, on the outshirts of Illaria.

The High Council of Sages met to discover some way to avert the formation of a Goblin Nation. Committed as they were to pure research, the Elves lack fighting forces and training in warfare. Furthermore, they are cut off from Jovian Falls, and can expect no assistance from the Duke.

The council was deliberating possible solutions when a messenger reported your party in the vicinity of Illaria. In urgent need of adventurers and mercenaries, they offered their hospitality, and now beg your assistance in the name of the entire Kingdom. Your assignment is to infiltrate the caverns, locate the treasure found by the Goblins, and destroy it. The Elves suspect that several hundred Goblins still remain in the caverns and they warn that you should not attempt to drive them out or kill them, for surely they will be more than a match for your party. Simply enter, search, and destroy.

DM ONLY: If the party declines the initial offer, the Elves will offer the party an ancient artifact in return for their services. The Elven community has been under seige from the Goblins and desperately needs the services of the party.

The Artifact offered is a set of eight magical rings. All rings may be worn by one individual or the set may be split up among several individuals. In any case, the powers of each ring will function for its wearer.

THE RUBY RING will allow the wearer to see all invisible, out of phase, hidden, astral, or etherial creatures within a range of 100 yards. This power functions automatically; the wearer need not concentrate on it. Also, an Invisibility spell of 30' radius can be cast three times per day from the ring.

THE EMERALD RING enables its wearer to teleport, once per day, without error to any location where he has spent at least 15 minutes previously. He may also teleport with up to five other people by joining hands with them; in no case can more than 200 lbs. of inanimate matter be teleported.

THE SAPPHIRE RING may only be safely worn for three one-hour periods a day. The Ring endows its wearer with all Elven abilities. If worn for more than an hour, the wearer will lose consciousness for 24 hours; unless a Wish is used, the wearer cannot be revived ahead of time.

THE TURQUOISE RING endows its wearer with free action (as the Rug of Free Action) and the ability to survive without air (or in a poisonous atmosphere) for three hours per day.

THE TOPAZ RING allows its wearer to cast the following spells three times per day: Light, Dancing Lights, and Fireball. In addition, these spells can be cast once per day: Continual Light and Flame Strike. All spells are cast at eighth level of effectiveness.

THE CORAL RING allows the wearer to regenerate 1 HTK/round, but will not restore points lost below zero nor will it regenerate lost limbs. This ring also grants a +3 bonus to saving throws vs. magic.

THE DIAMOND RING allows its wearer to cast each of the following spells three times per day: Rope Trick, Minor Creation, and Maze.

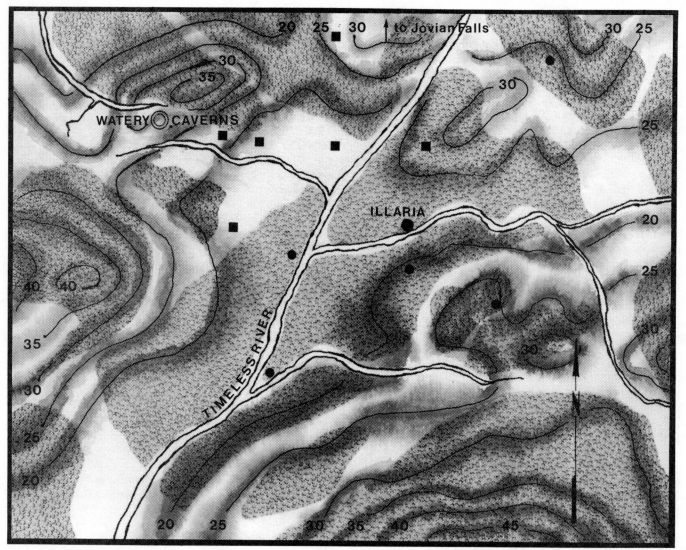

scale: |___50 mi.___|

— altitude in hundreds of feet

destroyed elven settlement ■ 　　　　**forest** 　　　　**elven settlement** ●

THE JADE RING allows its wearer to cast the following spells once per day: Stun, Power Word Blind, and Power Word Kill.

The rings possess one side effect not mentioned by the Council: After six months absence from Illaria, the rings will Geas their owners to return and remain in Illaria. The rings, once the Geas has been cast, may not be removed except by Elven Clerics.

The Elves will allow the party to take the rings with them when they attack the Goblin caverns, and, if the party is successful, the party will be allowed to keep them. If the party has not reported back to Illaria within 30 days, the Elves will assume that the party has died or did not undertake the task; in any case, they will magically summon the rings back to Illaria.

DM NOTE: Have the group decide if they will undertake the task, and then read them one of the following paragraphs:

Accepted Challenge:

Since you have accepted the challenge, a small group of Elves will guide you to the Watery Caverns, and wait for your return to guide you back. They will not enter the caverns. The caverns are approximately 150 miles away and the journey should take eight days. The council wants you to begin tomorrow night; in nine days the moon will be new (absent from the sky) and you will have a better chance to slip in unseen. Until then, all your needs will be tended to.

Didn't Accept Challenge:

Since you have decided not to take the challenge, the Council is greatly saddened, but makes no further attempt to force you. They ask that you leave Illaria as quickly as possible (tomorrow afternoon), attempt to reach Jovian Falls, the closest large city, and seek assistance on their behalf.

88

DM NOTE: If the party should decide not to take on the assignment, allow them to leave. A handy Goblin patrol of 100 or so will capture them, take them to the Watery Caverns and enslave them. At this point, they should be given the opportunity to escape just as if they had entered on their own accord and been captured. If, upon their escape, they leave the Caverns and do not attempt to seek out the source of the Goblin secret, they will surely run into additional patrols. Naturally, the Goblins will be in hot pursuit.

DM'S HISTORY OF THE WATERY CAVERNS

This natural, volcanic cavern complex was first discovered by Troglodytes and became their lair. They grew and prospered for thousands of years in the caverns. On the eve of the second War of Goblinkind, all the Troglodytes were summoned by their King to help form a Troglodyte army. Several thousand Troglodytes left the caverns and marched toward Lake Leopold, the gathering place of the army. They never made it. Within a day of their departure, all Troglodytes lay dead—emaciated and horribly shriveled. The nearby groups of Dwarves, Kobolds, and Trolls viewed the occurance as a bad omen and left the region. For centuries, the caverns lay deserted and unused except by the non-intelligent denizens of the region.

About two thousand years ago, the Grand Master of Elven Learning travelled through the area and was greatly impressed with the beauty of a giant redwood forest. He and his small group of scribes and apprentices settled in the region and established a College of Nature Studies. Years passed, and the elven population increased, as the reputation of the elven scholars spread throughout the land and to other continents. Hundreds of Elves travelled to Illaria, as the community was called, to take up their studies and, in time, Illaria became the center of all elven learning.

Once the necessary work of settling in and beginning the establishment of the college was completed, the Grand Master ordered that the surrounding regions be explored and charted. The caverns were rediscovered and the various levels summarily investigated. The elven exploratory team named them the Watery Caverns due to their damp and wet nature, and the presence of two small lakes on the second level. Disliking the atmosphere of the caverns, the Elves' investigation was cursory, and no effort was made to chart them. Nothing of value could be found therein; the complex was inhabited only by stray Rats, Bats, Giant Spiders, and Centipedes. The caverns remained barren for several hundred years thereafter.

About 1400 years ago, a lone Mine Dwarf settled in the upper level of the caverns. He mined the caverns for a few decades, but the dank atmosphere of the caverns was not conductive to hard labor, and eventually he became morose, cantankerous, and completely mad. He never left the confines of the caverns.

The Elves became aware of his presence and sent a small delegation to see if they could be of any assistance to him. The Dwarf chased them off in a fury, ranting that they were there to steal his discovery, to leech his soul, and bring about his death. The Elves left and never returned, though they did keep a watchful eye over the caverns.

Seven hundred years passed, and still the Dwarf lived.

The elven scouting parties that patrolled the area reported that the could hear his voice bellowing forth from the caverns, hysterical, uncoherent, and raving. Finally, 721 years after he moved in, the Dwarf was found by an Elven patrol, not more than a hundred yards from the entrance of the caverns. He was dead, his body emaciated and shrunken, the skin petrified.

The Grand Master declared that the caverns were not to be entered until proper precautions could be taken to insure the sanity of those entering, for obviously some great evil lurked within, stealing minds and souls. As the Illarian community grew, there never seemed enough time to do more than ponder the nature of the Watery Caverns.

The complex remained empty until, eleven years ago, it was discovered by a wandering band of Goblins. The Goblins found it to be suitably depressing and vile—just the environment they favored—and without further ado, moved in. Suddenly they discovered that all signs of aging seemed to stop. They became convinced that they had discovered some great magical stronghold, and their numbers rapidly increased.

Four years after they moved in, the Goblins discovered a secret passage that led to a hitherto undiscovered cavern network (undiscovered by everyone, but the Dwarf). The ground of this cavern consisted of soft, pliant, rainbow-colored clay. Overjoyed, the Goblins concluded that they had found their place of creation and began to search in earnest for the Well of Life, which they knew to be nearby. Their search was successful, and the Well was discovered in a huge cavern at the end of a secret underwater passage. A hole was drilled into a cavern floor (above the underwater passage) and a ceremonial altar was built above it to conceal the entrance.

As the Goblin population continued to increase, the Chief announced that it was time to unify all the Goblins and form a Goblin nation. Naturally, he would plan the conquest and serve as the leader of the new nation. Emboldened by their apparent undying nature which they attributed (correctly) to the waters of the Well of Life, they attacked the elven capital of Illaria. The Elves were able to turn back the assault, but not before many lives were lost. An elven trading caravan to Jovian Falls was intercepted, and the one surviving Elf was taken into slavery.

THE WELL OF LIFE

The Well of Life is an ancient artifact of the Elder Gods, created in a time before the advent of the gods that are worshipped at present. Although legends exist about the Well, no one knew its location, though thousands of adventurers were sent to seek it out. The Well is sentient, possessing the soul of the last elder god. Imbedded in the floor of the Well is a gem, which contains the soul of the demon goddess Borzsanna.

POWERS OF THE WELL

1   Drinking from its waters (one pint) will restore all lost hit points and neutralize all poisons. This may be done as often as one wishes, with no ill effects.

2   Immersing the remains of a newly slain corpse (within

1 week of death) will resurrect the body.

3 Immersing the body of a long slain creature will cause the body to be slowly reformed in another shape (use reincarnation chart).

4 Continued drinking of the water (a full week) will bring about changes in the body, causing it to never age. Unfortunately, if one ceases to drink the water, his body will attempt to readjust itself for 1-6 days. After this period, one must continue drinking the water (at least one pint per day) or the non-aging effects will be reversed. Should the imbiber refrain from drinking the water for but 1 additional day (24 hours), he will suddenly revert to his true age. Additionally, Goblins and Hobgoblins who stop drinking the water for just seven days will suddenly age very rapidly (the water dissolved the act of their creation). They will age so rapidly that they will die from old age within three days unless they again drink of water from the well.

5 The water may be transported in any container, but after 1-12 hours all resurrecting powers of the water will be lost. It will, however, continue to heal all damage and avert the effects of aging for another 30 days.

6 Over the years, natural movement of the earth has caused cracks in the side of the Well. Its water constantly spills forth, serving as the source of a river and many springs. The non-aging effects of the water, are potent only in the immediate area of the caverns, by the time the water emerges from the mountain, all magical properties have been lost.

This meant that the Troglodytes and the Dwarf, who had drunk of the waters for many hundreds of years, immediately died of old age when deprived of the magical water. The Troglodytes had been unaware of this side effect, but the Dwarf, of a more curious and persistant nature, had discovered the Well, solved the riddle which allowed him to communicate with the god spirit of the well, and learned of the water's properties. This discovery convinced the Dwarf that he would never leave the caverns; should he depart and be unable to return, he knew he would die. This knowledge brought about his madness, and eventual death. Fearing that the elven patrol sought to kill him, he decided to set traps around the entrance to the caverns. Once outside, he was blinded by the sunlight which he had not seen for 700 years and could not find his way back to the caverns. Twenty-four hours later, the water's effects reversed, and old age claimed his life.

WATERY CAVERNS — LEVEL 1

A The entrance to the complex is well-guarded. There are two alert Goblin sentries posted outside and they are accompanied by four Dire Wolves. The guards are on duty both day and night. Cavern A is unfurnished and contains six additional Goblin guards commanded by an Elder. If openly attacked, they will immediately wind a horn, alerting the fighting forces in Caverns B, C, and D. Each guard is armed with 1d4 throwing casks filled with contact poison; see Cavern 12 on Level 3 for details.
Six Goblin Guards [AC: 5, HTK: 7, 5, 4, 6, 7, 4, 3, 2 (1d8)]
Goblin Elder [AC: 3, HTK: 17 (3d8-3)]
Two Dire Wolves [AC: 6, HTK: 21, 17 (3d8+3)]

B-C These two caverns serve as barracks for the Goblin fighting forces guarding the entrance to the cavern complex. There are 25 piles of sleeping furs in each cavern to accommodate the fighters, several barrels (containing water) and several large clay pots (containing food). The fifty guards, usually occupied in playing knuckle-bones, are not overly alert, feeling that they will be alerted should the need arise. Each guard has 1d10 coppers; the leaders have 2d12 silver pieces. There are always 4 Elders, 6 Leaders, and 10 Dire Wolves present.

4 Goblin Elders [AC: 3, HTK: 17, 19, 15, 11 (3d8-3)]

6 Goblin Leaders [AC: 4, HTK: 9, 13, 15, 14, 13, 14 (2d8-2)]

10 Dire Wolves [AC: 6, HTK: 21, 18, 17, 13, 16, 18, 11, 21, 14, 20 (3d8)]

50 Goblin Fighters [AC: 7, HTK: 5 each (1d8+1)]

D   This large cavern is used primarily to store foodstuffs gathered from the surrounding forests. Animal carcasses are suspended from poles, and large quantities of edible roots are set out to dry in large nets suspended above the floor.

    The ceiling is over 100' high and, if examined closely, a ledge that runs almost the entire perimeter of the cavern will be noted. This ledge appears to be separated from the rest of the cavern by a wooden screen. Behind the screens, twelve large hulking shapes can be seen squatting on the ledges. These are the Goblins' pet Cockatrices. If an alarm is raised and the invaders cannot be repelled, the Cockatrices will be released, allowing the Goblins to retreat to the lower levels to regroup.

Twelve Cockatrices [AC: 5, HTK: 20 each (5d8)]

E   This is the holding area for all the slaves. The entire area is filled with small wooden cages, each housing a single slave. A number of slaves hang from chains on the walls. There are approximately 100 slaves, and they are all in extremely poor condition. Suspended from the ceiling on ropes are 10 large barrels filled with oil. If the party advances in this direction, the ropes will be cut by the guards, drenching the slaves. Several fire arrows will then be shot into the room by the retreating guards, setting the soaked slaves on fire.

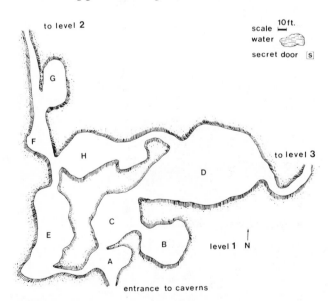

to level 2

scale 10 ft.

water

secret door [S]

to level 3

to level 1 N

entrance to caverns

F-G These are not normally inhabited or used by the Goblins. These rubble-filled caverns each contain a large hole in the outer wall about 3' in diameter. These are two of the numerous escape tunnels that the Goblins can use to escape the complex. A typical Goblin tactic is to retreat to the surface and then re-enter the complex and ambush the invaders from

behind, cutting off their retreat. These Goblin escape tunnels are too small for humans or elves to use, unless they crawl.

H   This is used by the Goblins to store the weapons and armor taken from their victim's bodies. There are 6 suits of leather armor (1 halfling size, 2 dwarf size, 3 man size), 5 suits of chainmail, (all human size), 7 small shields, 6 large shields, and 2 sets of platemail (human size). There are a great variety of weapons in piles about the cavern (20% chance of finding any particular type of weapon). None of the armor or weapons are magical, but are otherwise of fine to excellent quality.

    A large array of clay and pottery jars are stacked in one corner. These jars contain the poisons that the Goblins manufacture (see section of poisons in the Goblin text). There will be 1d6 jars of each type poison on hand at all times. Also, there are 2d12 small casks filled with contact poison; the Goblins throw these at intruders.

LEVEL 2

DM ONLY: This large second level is the primary food-growing are for the tribe. It is important, for it contains (in Room 9) the secret underwater tunnel to the Well of Life. If the party has managed to enter without raising an alarm, there will be no set encounters on this level. Refer to the Random Monster Encounter Table only. There is a possibility of a random monster encounter every 1/2 hour, on a roll of 1d6. Small vermin naturally congregate whereever large quantities of food are present.

    The intersection at Area 8, if examined, will reveal that the path heading east (to Room 9) has been worn smooth by the shuffling of many feet over its surface. This should alert the party that there is something of interest there. The presence of the altar should reinforce this conclusion, but no further clues should be given.

1   This relatively small cavern is the lair of two Shriekers. The Goblins feed the Shriekers regularly in order to keep them in the area as a security measure. Any light source in the cavern will activate the Shriekers and alert the Hobgoblin guards in Cavern 7A.

Shriekers [AC: 7, HTK: 22, 16 (3d8)]

2   This small cavern is populated by two Trappers. One is located in the center of the room, the other directly in the entrance of the tunnel leading to Area 3. The Goblins feed both creatures and occasionally drop small coins or gems for them to add to their hoard. Treasure worth 2d100 gp will be found in a hole under one of the Trappers.

2 Trappers [AC: 3, HTK: 58, 89 (12d8)]

3   This cavern is totally empty and unused. The secret tunnel in the north wall was constructed by the Hermit Dwarf, but has not been discovered by the Goblins.

4   This small cavern is unused by the Goblins. It contains some early carvings of the Hermit Dwarf. The four

pieces of sculpure in this cavern, all life-sized Dwarven statues, have a value of 1500 gp each. The statues are 4' tall, weigh about 400 lbs. each. If the party carelessly attempts to chip them from the floor, there is a 65% chance that the statue will shatter.

5 These cavern areas (as well as the areas marked 5a) were the source of the cavern complex's name. Each area is filled with stagnant and malodorous water 1d12 feet in depth. The water is not fit to drink.

5a These two large caverns contain small lakes. The water is filthy and both caverns have an unpleasant, though not overpowering, odor. There is a 75% chance that at any time there will be 1d4 small boats on the shore. There is a small, totally barren island near the center of the western lake.

6 These small, empty caverns are unused by the Goblins. There is a 45% chance that each cavern investigated will hold a random monster (see Wandering Monster Table).

7 If the party enters this cavern without adequate light, there is a 75% chance that they will believe it to be occupied by a large assortment of monsters. Every inch of the rock walls and ceiling is covered with the Dwarven Hermits' carvings, dating from his later years after he had lost his sanity. There are Ogres, Trolls, Goblins, Kobolds, Giants, Snakes, and Medusas along the walls, with a giant carving of a Roc covering the ceiling. Its gigantic wings are spread as if in flight and long talons descend toward the ground.

Behind a secret panel in the ceiling, within the body of the Roc, the Dwarf's treasure hoard will be found: 111 sapphires, each worth 1d20x10 gp.

7a This is the only guardpost on the entire level. It is manned by four Hobgoblin Tribal Elders.
4 Hobgoblins [AC: 2, HTK: 24, 23, 21, 25 (3d8+3)]

8 This small cavern is formed by the convergence of 6 tunnels. If examined carefully, the party will notice that the path leading to Area 9 is worn smooth.

9 This cavern houses the only entrance to the Well of Life. There is a warm, slow underground river flowing through the cavern. The river flows to the northeast eventually passing through chamber 11. The underwater tunnel leading to the Well of Life is hidden under an altar at point Z. Hiding in areas X and Y are two 7th skill Shamans. They will attack the party if they locate the secret entrance (or if they are discovered); otherwise, they will wait silently.

DESCRIPTION OF ALTAR: At point Z, on the far side of the river, a large round altar stands. Constructed of blocks of polished volcanic rock, the altar is 5' tall and apparently quite solid. If a thief looks for secret doors on the eastern wall of the cavern at the point nearest the altar, he has his normal chance to find a small, hidden sliding door. Only 6" square, the door conceals a small lever; pulling the lever will open the southern face of the altar. The center of the altar is hollow and a shaft has been sunk into the volcanic rock below. Anyone looking into the shaft will note that the shaft ends at a river's surface about eight feet below; hand and toe holds descend to the waterline.

The secret underwater tunnel is 5' in diameter and extremely dark. It will take 12 rounds to travel the distance to the other side if the party wishes to swim. Each round, there is a 1% (cumulative every round) chance that the individual will panic and inhale water.

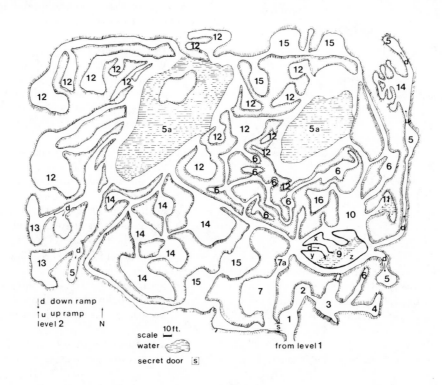

d down ramp
u up ramp
level 2   N

scale [—] 10 ft.
water
secret door [s]

from level 1

If this occurs, he will drown in 1d4 rounds unless dragged to shore or given assistance. If the party swims or searches near the top of the tunnel, there is a 50% chance per person, that a guide rope will be discovered. Anyone using the guide rope to pull themselves along will cover the distance in half the time.

The far side of the tunnel opens up into a small pool in a large cavern (refer to well level for a description of this area).

10 This large cavern contains many stalagtites, stalagmites, and columns; water constantly seeps through the layers of limestone rock above and drips from the ceiling and walls. There are no Piercers in this area, although from all appearances, there should be.

11 The runoff from area 10 trickles into the river in this small cavern. Limestone coats the floor of the passage and the cavern, making walking treacherous. Any who slip and fall into the river at this point are lost forever, for the underground flow has no known exit.

12 These caverns serve as Mushroom Farms for the Goblins. The mushrooms grow to a height of 14 to 24 inches, are quite palatable, and grow rapidly year round. There is a 15% chance of a wandering monster in each cavern explored.

13 These caverns are sealed with large, tightfitting doors made of thin strips of wood and leather. Within the chamber, the Goblins raise huge quantities of large, white worms, a favored food source. The caverns are filled with a 1d4 inch deep mixture of worms, mulch and mushrooms at all times. The worms can grow to a length of 40 inches and are quite nourishing (though palatable only to Goblins).

14 These areas are used for the cultivation of a fragrant rock moss that grows rapidly and can be harvested daily. The moss is quite nutritious when eaten raw; its nutlike fruit can be dried, ground, and baked into bread, though the Goblins prefer to eat it raw.

15 These large caverns are used as additional storage for game that was hunted and brought down from the surface. The meat is hung to dry on racks along the walls and form hooks set in the ceilings. A wide variety of animals can be seen here. There are also a number of human and demi-human bodies—Goblin slaves that did not survive.

16 This large cavern is filled with rubble and ignored by the Goblins. In this area, the Hermit Dwarf discovered a rich vein of gems; much wealth remains, if the players are inclined to mine. The Dwarf hid the rich vein and it will take another dwarf or gnome to spot its location.

LEVEL 3

DM NOTE: Unless otherwise indicated, all the Goblins on this level are ordinary Goblins with 1d8-1 HTK and AC: 7. There are very few Shamans or Witchdoctors in the complex, and most of those who remain are on the Well Level.

1 This is the only entrance to the Goblin tribes's living area; the southern passage leads to level 1. There are 12 Goblin guards on duty here at all times. The room is barren except for a few furs littering the ground. There are two guards posted at each exit and the others are usually to be found reclining on the furs or playing knucklbones near the center of the room.

2 This large cavern is the barracks of the fighting force on duty for the day. There are 40 hammocks slung among the numerous outcroppings of rock, and many woven mats and furs are scattered about the floor. There are 5d10+10 Goblins in this area at all times. In addition, there are also 5 Goblin Elders [AC: 5, HTK: 18, 21, 16, 13, 15 (3d8-3)]. The Goblins are awake, working on their weapons and discussing plans for uniting all the Goblins.

3 This cavern serves as the quarters for the off-duty Goblin guards. It is virtually identical to cavern 2, except that the 5d20+20 Goblins are asleep. The off-duty elders sleep in Cavern 6. If invaded, the group will retreat to Cavern 12. They will then spring a trap in the center of the corridor which will bring an avalanche of rock down, cutting off the corridor entirely.

4 This gigantic cavern is the common quarters of the tribe, the area in which all ceremonies are conducted, food is cooked, leather is worked, and the chief and Shaman officiate. There are 3d20 Goblins and 2d10 Hobgoblins [AC: 4, HTK: 1d8+1) in this area. If the complex is invaded, the females and offspring will be hearded into area 15 with a small force of 3d20 Goblins to protect them. The remainder of the Goblins and Hobgoblins will flee out the escape tunnels in Caverns 7, 8, 10, and 12, climb to the surface, and enter the complex to attack the intruders from behind. It will take them 3-12 rounds to return.

5 This is the tribal living area. The entire area is littered with hammocks, palettes, chests, crates, and other household items; space is almost non-existant. The complex currently contains 400 females and 700 offspring who will congregate in this area, as far from the entrance as possible, when attackers are spotted. Many large boxes are stored along the walls leading to Cavern 4; when all have retreated inside, the boxes will be toppled, effectively sealing the entrance for 2-8 2-8 rounds. Naturally, there will be a large opening near the ceiling, through which spells may be cast.

The chests and crates contain the spare weapons, finished leather goods, and personal possessions of the Goblins. They contain a total of 1000 gp worth of coins, jewelry, and gems. The leather goods can be sold for an additional 5000 gp.

6   This cavern serves to house the Goblin Elders and Leaders. It is also extremely crowded with boxes and personal possessions. If the party digs through the stacks, they will find reasure equivalent to that contained in Cavern 5. Four Leaders [AC: 5, HTK: 7, 10, 9, 13 (2d8-2)] and six Elders [AC: 5, HTK: 19, 17, 14, 15, 15, 20 (3d8-3)] are in this cavern.

7
8   These caverns are the residences of the lesser Shamans and all the Witchdoctors of the tribe. Their quarters contain few personal effects and are less cramped. There is no treasure here, for all the Shamans and Witchdoctors are currently on the Well level.

9   This spacious cavern is the living quarters of the Hobgoblin Tribal Chieftain/War Leader. He shares it with his personal guards and his "harem for the day." There are several chest along the southern wall containing leather goods, small weapons, and a personal treasure trove. His hoard of 2000 gp, 17 pp, 2500 cp, 1000 gp worth of gems and jewelry is stashed in a Bag of Holding, which is folded and concealed inside a vile-smelling sock (the entire chest is filled with reeking unwashed clothing). The Chief also has a +2 wooden shield, and a +2 longsword.
Chief [AC: 2, HTK: 39 (5d8+5)]
4 Hobgoblin Guards [AC: 4, HTK: 30, 27, 25, 29 (4d8+4)]

10   This is the private quarters of the Tribal Shaman and his personal assistants. Like all the other living areas, this cavern is filled to overflowing with personal effects. The tribal treasure, consisting of gems worth 25,000 gp and jewelry worth 37,000 gp is hidden in a hidden hole in the floor. The bag holding the jewels has been thoroughly seeped in contact poison; any who touch the bag with bare flesh must save vs. poison (at -4) or die immediately. Four Shamans [AC: 8, Level 4, HTK: 20, 18, 21, 22 (3d8-1)] are in this cavern.

11   This cavern is used by the Goblins for the punishment of uncooperative slaves and execution of their criminals. Braziers of coals, pincers, and other torture implements are scattered throughout the cavern. Several Goblins and demi-humans are currently being tortured; they are hanging on the walls and the ceilings. Several bodies litter the floor.

12   This area contains all the implements and ingredients used by the Goblins to manufacture poisons. There are tables, presses, cartons, barrels, and racks crammed into every corner. Ingredients fill the shelves and boxes to overflowing while barrels of the finished product are stacked near the northern entrance. Many small casks of contact poison are stacked in a niche in the west wall; when hurled, these casks do 1-2 HTK of damage, shatter easily, and cause all individuals splashed with the contents to save vs. poison or go into convulsions in 1d4 rounds (death follows in 2d4 rounds). It is 45% likely that any group of Goblins numbering more than 20 will have 1d12 casks with them. All guards posted are automatically equipped with a minimum of 1d20+10 casks.

THE WELL LEVEL

The secret underwater tunnel leads to a gigantic cavern, 150 feet by 300 feet. The floor of the cavern is multicolored clay, ranging through all the colors of the rainbow. In the center of the cavern is a small 5' diameter well. It is constructed of blocks of stone so carefully hewn and fitted, mortar was not needed to hold them together. Close to the Well are nine Shamans occupied with the task of storing water in large casks and leather pouches. They are assisted by seven Witchdoctors. Four Hobgoblin Elders stand guard near the entrance to this cavern.

4 level 4 Shamans [AC: 9, HTK: 19, 22, 23, 22 (3d8-1)]
2 level 5 Shamans [AC: 9, HTK: 24, 26 (3d8+3)]
1 level 6 Shaman [AC: 9, HTK: 4d8-1)]
2 level 7 Shamans [AC: 9, HTK: 30, 32 (4d8+3)]

3 level 2 Witchdoctors [AC:8, HTK: 8, 6, 9 (1d8+1)]
2 level 3 Witchdoctors [AC: 9, HTK: 9, 8 (1d8+2)]
2 level 4 Witchdoctors [AC: 9, HTK: 8, 10 (1d8+3)]

6 Elders [AC: 2, HTK: 17, 15, 19, 20, 19, 21 (3d8-3)]

Runic symbols are carved into the rock comprising the base of the Well. The writing is extremely ancient, and a Read Magic spell is required to decipher it. It translates as follows:

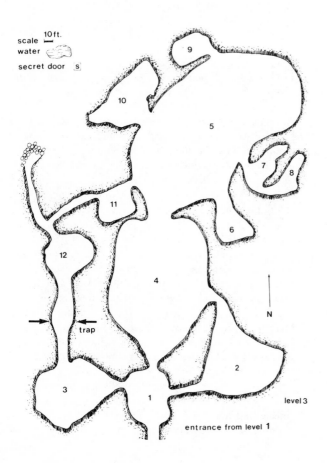

scale   10 ft.
water
secret door   s

9
10
5
7   8
11
6
12
4
N
trap
2
3
1
level 3
entrance from level 1

Speak the names of the elder gods,
Call upon their aid,
Call upon the sleeping lord,
He your lives will save.

Inside the Well, one foot below the rim, a similar set of runes is inscribed. They are visible only to someone climbing down into the Well. If a Read Magic is cast upon these runes, the following will be read:

rowdnlid, thoelradr, eslraod, dieflror,
racoetr, aysler, and preseigllnod

These are anagrams for windlord, earthlord, sealord, firelord, creator, slayer, and sleeping lord. If these deciphered names are recited as directed (first the names of the elder lords, followed by "sleeping lord"), the soul of the Phaucet, the ancient god inhabiting the artifact will be aroused.

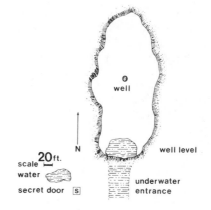

Once he is informed of the situation, Phaucet will inform the party that although they cannot destroy the Well, they can stop the Goblin threat by temporarily shutting off their supply of Well water. The Well serves as the source for a river and many springs in the area, but the flow can be stopped. Phaucet will reveal that pulling a lever, situated at the bottom, of the Well 200' below the surface, will temporarily cut off the water source. This emergency cutoff will automatically reset itself in 30 days, but the party should be able to survive by drinking from the numerous casks during the dry spell.

NOTE TO DM: Naturally, this will have the desired effect for the Goblins will all age rapidly and die at the end of a week. The caverns will slowly dry out if the party fixes the Well, but this will deprive the countryside of a major source of water.

Phaucet will only reveal the major powers of the Well to a character of true neutral alignment. He will caution that these powers must be used wisely, for neither good nor evil may rule the world nor disrupt the balance (as the Goblins were attempting to do).

At this point, the party has these choices: They can try to prevent the Goblins from entering the cavern for water until they all die, they can enter the Well and pull the lever, or they can leave and call for assistance.

The party should be able to easily defend the opening to the secret underground entrance to the Well level. The most dangerous action the party can perform is to leave for more assistance, for the Goblins will have an additional 4-6 weeks to prepare for the invasion of another large force (the caverns area is in an isolated location). The Goblins who left the complex to take the news to the other tribes will not present a threat; they have been absent from the caverns long enough for the aging effects to kill them.

Should the party chose to descend into the Well, it is very likely (65%) that a large gem, imbedded in the bottom, will be discovered. Phaucet, if asked, knows nothing of the gem and will want it removed.

This gem is, of course, Borzanna's soul gem. If the stone is pried loose, it will probably (80%) shatter and Borzsanna will appear to attack the party. Without the protection of the gem, however, she can be slain.

ENCOUNTER TABLES FOR
THE ILLARIAN FOREST INTRIGUE

WILDERNESS ENCOUNTERS

1   1-12 Giant Goats [AC: 7, 3d8+1 HTK]
2   2-8   Badgers [AC: 4, 1d8+2 HTK]
3   3-11 Mountain Trolls [AC: 3, 8d8+6 HTK]
4   3-8   Brown Bears [AC: 6, 5d8+5 HTK]
5   2-5   Jackalwere [AC: 4, 4d8 HTK]
6   1-4   Manticore [AC: 4, 6d8+3 HTK]
7   1-6   Wyvern [AC: 3, 7d8+7 HTK]
8   1-4   Gorillas [AC: 6, 6d8 HTK]

CAVERN ENCOUNTERS

1   2-20 armed Goblin Guards [AC: 7, 1d8-1 HTK]
2   1-2   Rust Monsters [AC: 2, 5d8 HTK]
3   4-16 Centipedes [AC: 9, 1d4 HTK]
4   1-10 Giant Rats [AC: 7, 1d4 HTK]
5   1-10 Stirges [AC: 8, 1d8+1 HTK]
6   2-6   Doppelgangers [AC: 5, 4d8 HTK]
7   1-6   Giant Toads [AC: 6, 2d8+2 HTK]
8   2-8   Su-Monsters [AC: 6, 5d8+5 HTK]
9   2-24 unarmed Goblins gathering food [AC: 7,
          1d8-1 HTK]
10 1-20 Giant Wasps [AC: 4, 4d8 HTK]
11 1-10 armed Goblin Guards [AC: 7, 1d8-1 HTK]
12 1-4   Phase Spiders [AC: 7, 5d8+5 HTK]